THE BOYS' BOOK OF
ROCKS AND FOSSILS

A rainbow produced by the spray from the Victoria Falls

THE BOYS' BOOK OF
ROCKS AND FOSSILS

I. O. EVANS F.R.G.S.
Member of the
Geologists' Association

BURKE  LONDON

ACKNOWLEDGMENTS

THE author and publishers wish to thank the following for permission to reproduce photographs and drawings and for advice and assistance in the preparation of this book:

The Geological Survey and the Ordnance Survey for their photographs of the scenery of Great Britain and their map of Glamorgan which are Crown Copyright and are reproduced by permission of the Controller of H.M. Stationery Office; the Agent General of Queensland; Allen & Unwin Ltd.; the Arizona Development Board; The British Museum (Natural History, (illustrations from *The Succession of Life through Geological Time* and *British Caenozoic Fossils*)); the British Travel & Holidays Association; the French Government Tourist Office; C. E. Hall & Son; the High Commissioner for the Federation of Rhodesia and Nyasaland; the Iceland Tourist Information Bureau; the Northern Ireland Tourist Board; Dr. J. E. Prentice; the Shell Photographic Unit; Dr. F. Smithson; the Swiss National Tourist Office; the United States Information Service and the Yugoslav National Tourist Office.

The author also wishes to thank Miss Naomi Galinski for assistance in the preparation of this book.

Burke Publishing Co. Ltd.
14 John Street, London, W.C.1.
Printed in Great Britain by
C. Tinling & Co. Ltd., Liverpool, London & Prescot.

Contents

CHAPTER I

The Science of the Earth

GEOLOGY IS the science of the earth, not only as it is but as it used to be. It describes the scenery around us and explains how it was formed; it describes the scenery of long ago and explains how it has changed. It examines the rocks to find out what they are made of and how they were made. It examines the fossils, the remains of living creatures buried in the rocks, to find out what sort of creatures they were, what sort of lives they lived and how they are related to those of the present day.

It is a science which is useful to miner and farmer, town-planner and engineer, and even to the camper seeking a site for his tent. It helps us to understand this surprising world. It can, if you wish, give you fascinating objects to collect and intriguing problems to work out. If you are a cameraman or an artist it will supply you with fresh subjects to photograph or draw. If you are keen on natural history it will help you to understand the plants and animals of today by comparing them with others which have long since vanished from the face of the earth.

An Outdoor Science

Geology can take you to exciting places: into the mountains, over the moors, by the side of the river, along the shore, and down into mines and subterranean gulfs. It can send you wading through streams, clambering along cliff paths, or fighting your way through brambles to reach the rock-face. For geology is an outdoor science, and the geologist has to be an outdoor man, making strenuous hikes into wild country and returning with specimens that will give him hours of absorbing indoor work. A professional geologist prospecting for oil or ore may find himself investigating regions almost unknown. No exploring party is complete without its geologist; even when out at sea, he may have to investigate conditions upon or just under the ocean-bed.

Field-work

The real work of a geologist is "in the field". Here you can study the earth itself, you can collect specimens, and you can see how the rocks affect the scenery. Indoor work in museums, laboratories and libraries will supply the background information which makes field-work more interesting and satisfying.

Hiking Kit

Ordinary hiking kit is quite suitable for field work, except that, for clambering over rocks, slacks are better than shorts or a kilt. Quarries can be dusty or muddy, so wear old clothes; nailed or stout-soled boots are better than shoes, for they support the ankles in rough country. For carrying your gear and specimens, a rucksack holds more than a haversack and is easier to carry, but it is harder to reach and its size may tempt you to overload yourself. The haversack is easier to reach, but when it is loaded its sideways pull is uncomfortable.

An assistant field geologist determines the position of a rock layer at an outcrop

You will, of course, need a waterproof coat or cape, a spare pullover for use on the hill-tops or if you have to wait about, your map and compass—when you use this, keep it clear of your hammer-head—and, if you are likely to be out after dark, an electric torch.

Geological Gear

All scientific work demands proper records, so the most important part of your gear is your notebook: even if you are not collecting, you can make notes about the scenery. Ability to make rough sketches is very helpful, as is a camera.

If you are collecting, provide yourself you have to buy is a special *geological* hammer, weighing about twelve or sixteen ounces, with one end of its head square for tapping the rocks and the other having a chisel edge for splitting them. You will find it useful to brand the haft with a hot wire or a lens, marking short lines an inch apart on one side and your initials on the other.

You will also find it helpful to have a cold chisel (the ordinary woodworker's chisel is useless) and still more helpful to have two, so if one gets jammed in a rock you can work it out with the other. In loose soil or clay a trowel or broad-bladed knife will be more useful than the hammer.

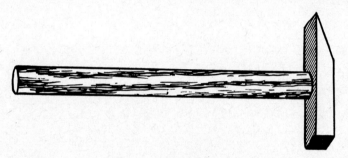

FIGURE I. *A geological hammer*

with plenty of wrapping-paper; or, better still, a good supply of small boxes. Number each specimen and wrap it up or box it carefully; and make an entry *at once* in your notebook recording just where you found the specimen and what you think it is. Specimens allowed to jostle about loose will soon be worthless and, unless you make your notes "on the spot", you will be amazed how soon, and how completely, you forget where your specimens came from. Don't make the mistake of collecting too much; geological specimens seem very heavy when carried far; in fact, unless you really want a specimen it is best to leave it where it is.

Geology does not need expensive or elaborate gear. Almost the only thing

Safety First

Your hammer needs judicious use; if you can find an experienced geologist to show you how to handle it, so much the better. A few gentle taps will be far more effective for breaking off a "hand specimen" than a heavy blow, which may send the rock splinters flying into your face and endanger your sight. A blow on a vertical cliff-face—and still more on an overhanging one—may cause a very dangerous fall of rock. A steep cliff-face may be easy to climb up but impossible to climb down, so there is a danger of getting trapped on a ledge. Even on gentler slopes you have to be careful, not only to find a safe foothold but to avoid any risk of making a scree collapse.

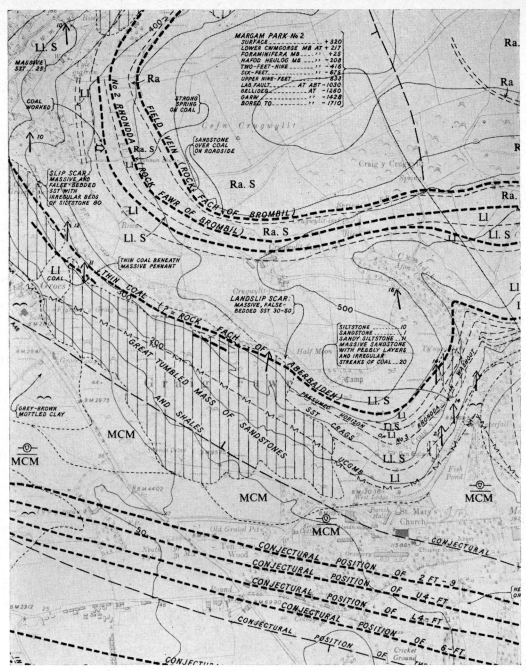

Part of a six-inch geological map of the South Wales Coalfield, showing boundaries of the outcrops (indicated by the faint dotted lines). The dark dotted lines show the probable positions of the coal seams. The small arrows and numbers indicate the direction and degree of dip. The letters indicate the beds to which the outcrops belong (for example: MCM means middle coal measures) and the dotted line accross the top right-hand corner indicates a fault

On the shore, there are two special dangers: wandering into a quicksand and being caught by the rising tide, so consult the local people before you cross a bay or go along the foot of the cliffs. If you are going into really wild country, the mountains or the moors, leave word what route you mean to follow and when you expect to get back. Caves and abandoned mine-workings too, have their own special dangers.

The Country Code

Interest in science is no excuse for trespassing, nor for breaking the Country Code. If you want to go on to private land to visit an exposure, ask permission first; otherwise you may find yourself turned off. Nor can you grumble if any specimens you have collected are confiscated or deliberately smashed: they belong to the owner of the land and not to you. Wherever you go, do no damage, leave no litter about, and especially no rock fragments; geologists have been banned from some interesting outcrops, and their work has been seriously hindered, simply because chippings left on the fields have injured the cattle.

Ask permission if you want to visit a quarry or other working; if you are allowed in, do as you are told and keep out of the way. If ordered under cover during blasting, remember this is meant for your safety, and resist any temptation to peep out at the big bang.

Studying the Rocks

Your compass will help you not only to find your way but to estimate the direction of dip—remembering, of course, that true dip is always perpendicular to the strike. Special clinometers are obtainable for measuring dip, but they are rather expensive. If you are a handyman you could perhaps make one out of a small spirit-level, a protractor and a folding ruler; otherwise, you will have to judge the dip by eye.

If you take a photograph of anything of geological interest, always use something to give the scale. If it is a small object, place a penny beside it; if it is rather larger, your geological hammer. If it is quite large, a quarry-face for example, get someone to stand in front of it.

Geological Maps

Though the one-inch-to-a-mile Ordnance map is best for finding your way, you will need a six-inch-to-the-mile outline map for charting the rocks. Mark on this the position of every exposure you come across, not forgetting such small ones as ditches, or the clues that the soil can give to the nature of the rocks below. Number each entry as you make it, and put the details in your notebook.

Before setting out on an expedition, it is well to consult the geological map of the region you mean to visit, and to "read it up"; you can usually consult maps and other sources of information at the local library or museum.

The maps show you not only the outcrops of various rocks, but also many of their exposures. Ability to read them comes with practice. On the edges of the maps you will find sections illustrating the build of the rocks. The vertical sections show the succession of the beds as revealed in borings; the horizontal ones show the structure of the rocks along a line which you will find indicated on the maps.

Identifying and Storing Specimens

You can identify your specimens by comparing them with those in local museums. You will have to find some way of storing them—a handyman could make a useful little cabinet, others less skilled will have to be content with cardboard boxes. But, however you store them, make sure that each is, so far as you can manage it, correctly named.

If ever you have to part with your specimens, do not just throw them away; give them to some other collector, to the local museum or to a school.

Indoor Work

During the long winter evenings, when field-work is impossible, a keen amateur geologist can find much to do. He has his specimens to re-arrange and study; and, from the rough notes he has made in the field, he can write up his observations. The library will supply him with books on various aspects of the subject.

Cheap books of exercises on geological maps are available. These show, in outline, imaginary stretches of country with the outcrops marked. It is an interesting task to draw sections across them illustrating their structure and then try to deduce the geological history of the region.

This indoor study is very useful, but its aim is to help you with your field-work. For this, after all, is the essential part of the science; just as you cannot understand astronomy without studying the sky, so you cannot understand geology without studying the earth.

"Geologese"

In studying geology, you will have to deal with long, unfamiliar words. This cannot be helped, for every subject has its own technical language and, if you do not know "geologese", you will find it hard to talk to other geologists or to read geological books.

There is no snobbery in science; geology has benefited much not only from university men but from self-educated stone-masons and canal-diggers—and a carpenter's daughter. So the language it uses is a queer mixture of long words and short. Some were devised by learned professors who, as usual, based them on Latin and Greek: some were those used by miners and quarrymen in their everyday work. So, along with words like "anticline" and "carboniferous", go others like "dip" and "fault". The term "lias" might puzzle you until you see the rocks it names and remember that it is a local pronunciation of "layers"; and "gault" puzzles everyone, for it is so old that nobody knows who first coined this name for a stiff, blue clay, or when or why it was first used.

Though the professors' words may be long and difficult, they have two great advantages over the simpler mining terms. Many of them almost explain themselves: in a "syncline" rock-beds slope "towards each other" and "metamorphic" is from the Greek for "changed in form". Moreover, these longer words are international, whereas the shorter ones are not, and you will find that helpful if you travel abroad or read foreign works. In a French book on geology, for example, words like *sedimentaire* will give you no trouble, but you will have to use a dictionary to find that *grès* means sandstone and that *une faille* is a fault.

You need not master every long word you meet. Many fossils, for example, have forbidding titles, but you will not need them unless you are going to collect and study them. On the other hand, you will find that in geology, as in many other sciences, some ordinary words are used with special meanings: "recent", for example, can mean thousands of years ago!

CHAPTER II

Rocks Formed Under Water

YOU PROBABLY think of a rock as being something very hard which holds firmly together. When a geologist speaks of rock what he means is any non-living substance, hard or soft, firm or loose, which helps to build the earth's crust, its outer layers. Chalk and granite are rocks, but so, in geologese, is a sandy beach or a tract of soft miry clay.

All rocks are made up of minerals, a few of one only, most of several—a mineral being something which usually has to be mined for. Unlike a rock, which may change in chemical composition from place to place, a mineral has the same composition everywhere. Chalk, for example, consists almost completely of calcite; and granite of three minerals, quartz, mica, and felspar.

Dip, Strike, Outcrop and Exposure

Many rocks are stratified—arranged in parallel layers—each layer forming one *stratum*, Latin for spread out. Where rock-beds are aslope, the direction in which they slope most steeply is their dip: it is measured in degrees from the horizontal line. Perpendicular to the dip is the strike: (if, as you read, you tilt this book towards you, keeping its lower edge flat

Current bedding in sandstone—Butley, Suffolk

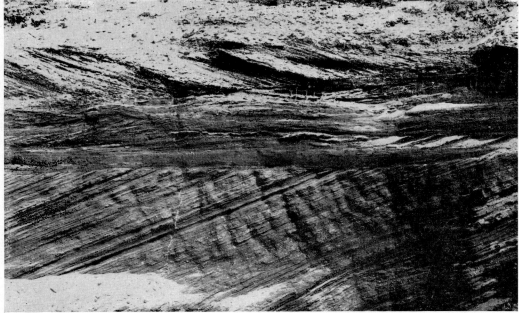

on the table, and imagine it to be a rock-bed, then a line straight down the print indicates its dip, and any line of print indicates its strike). When a rock-face is askew to the dip, the slope of its beds gives only an apparent dip, which is less than the true dip: this is a point about which geologists have to be careful.

The strike of a rock-bed shows its run, the direction in which it extends across

of material worn from the land. He explained that the waves carry it out to sea, and it slowly hardens on the sea-floor into solid rock. Later, this theory was worked out in more detail by a Roman Catholic bishop, Nicolas Steno.

Many rocks plainly consist of grains or larger pieces of stone like a hardened sediment. Some are so soft they fall to pieces at a touch; others are welded

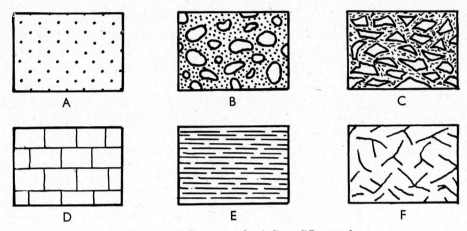

FIGURE 2. *Patterns used to indicate different rocks*

A. *Sand or sandstone*
B. *Conglomerate (pudding-stone)*
C. *Breccia*
D. *Limestone or chalk*
E. *Clay or shale*
F. *Granite*

country, which may be the same as the bed's outcrop. The outcrop is not only the place where the rock "crops out" on the surface of the ground, but the whole area where it is covered only by such superficial material as the soil, vegetation, buildings and so forth or, in some places, by a thickish layer of clay. The place where any rock is visible is an exposure: it may be anything from a cliff-face or a quarry to a ditch or the excavation for a telegraph pole.

Sedimentary Rocks

The famous artist Leonardo da Vinci, who was also a great scientist, was one of the first to realise that many rocks consist

together by a natural cement. These sedimentary rocks form most of the stratified rocks, and some of them, the free-stones, are naturally divided, by joints, into fair-sized rectangular blocks.

Rocks Formed of Hardened Sand

Sandstone is formed of grains of sand, which consists of the mineral silica, named from the Latin word for flint. Pure silica is white or colourless, but in many sandstones its grains are iron-stained brown, yellow or red, and in a few they are tinted green by the mineral glauconite. For example, the Coloured Sands of Alum Bay in the Isle of Wight are famous for the variety of their hues.

The grains in the different sandstones vary greatly in shape and size. Those which have been much blown about by the wind have rubbed one another smooth, but those from a river bed are rougher; a very rough sandstone, or one formed of very large grains, is a grit.

In many sandstones, the grains are held together by a cement consisting of limestone. When they are held in a silica of cement they form a quartzite, a rock so hard that a knife will not scratch it. Another characteristic of quartzite is that its newly-broken surfaces look rather greasy.

A sandstone that contains many pebbles is a conglomerate, sometimes known as pudding-stone, which is what it looks like. But one that contains not rounded pebbles but jagged fragments of rock is a breccia (an Italian word pronounced "brecha", and meaning the rubble from a broken wall). On the other hand, a very fine-grained sandstone is a siltstone.

Many sandstones show current bedding, the layers in an exposure sloping in different directions. This is due to changing sea-currents which swirled the accumulating sediments this way and that.

On the surface of a sheet of sandstone

ripple-marks left by the waves or pitted with rain-prints; it may bear the tracks of the birds that walked across it, the trails of sea-creatures that crawled over it, or the imprint of waving sea-weeds that brushed it.

Rocks Formed of Hardened Clay

Clay is another rock formed of very fine grains, but they are quite different from the grains in a siltstone. They consist of chemical compounds of silica, aluminium and water: these combine to produce a sticky plastic substance which becomes an unpleasant mud when damp but is solid and hard when dry.

A hardened clay is a mudstone, unless its grains are stratified, when it is a shale. Clay and shale may be almost any colour, from the pure white kaolin (china-clay) of Cornwall to the dark blue gault of south-east England, the blue lias of Lyme Regis, and the black fireclay which underlies many of the coal-seams.

Buried in many of the sandstones and shales you find fossils, the remains of extinct animals and plants. In some of the other sedimentary rocks these remains are so plentiful you might think there was more fossil than rock.

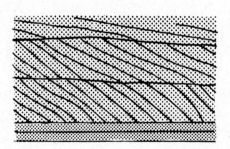

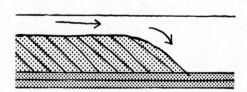

FIGURE 3.   *Current bedding*

A.   *As seen in an exposure*

B.   *Showing how the beds were formed*

you may find marks made upon it before it hardened, when it was still a beach at the edge of the sea. Like a modern beach, the surface may be grooved with

Rocks from Animal Remains: Limestone

Fossils abound in many of the limestones, rocks chiefly formed of the mineral

Ripple-marks in sandstone—Little Haven, Pembrokeshire

The results of salt-mining at Leftwich, Cheshire

calcite (calcium carbonate). Some are so very fossiliferous that they have special names: shelly limestones, crinoidal limestones and algal limestones respectively contain countless sea-shells, remains of those strange plant-like animals, the sea-lilies (crinoids), and remains of sea-weeds (algae). There are also coral limestones: some ranges of hills, like Wenlock Edge in Shropshire, largely consist of fossil coral-reefs.

Pure calcite is colourless or white, but in the limestone it is discoloured by impurities. So limestones may range in colour from off white to very dark, though most are brown or grey. They also differ in texture: oolite, though named after the Greek for egg, does not contain fossil eggs, it is limestone so very coarse-grained that it looks something like fish-roe; pisolite (pea-stone) is even more coarsely grained. Chert, the flinty material you find in limestone, is not calcite but a form of silica.

Apart from the fossils it contains, the calcite in the limestone is itself of organic origin—produced from the decaying remains of animals and plants. A young nineteenth-century student, Charles Lyell, who later became one of the world's great geologists, actually saw how it is formed. He was looking on when a lake was drained; on its floor was a thick bed of freshwater limestone; the workmen told him that this had not been there last time the lake was drained. Here was a rock which had formed within living memory: its upper layers were loose and powdery, but the further from the top they were the harder they had become; the lowest part had been transformed into solid limestone.

Rocks from Animal Remains: Chalk

Chalk is a soft fine-grained limestone, in which the calcite is almost pure. When freshly broken it is white, but its surface soon gets discoloured by the weather and, in one or two places, it is stained red with iron. Not only may you find sizable fossils in it; if you powder it and examine it under a microscope you will see that it contains some very tiny fossils and looks almost exactly like ooze, a whitish mud dredged up from the bottom of the sea. (Blackboard chalk is not real chalk, it is a synthetic material, calcium sulphate.)

Chalk contains two other minerals. The flints are great rounded nodules of silica, mostly arranged in rows parallel to the bedding of the chalk; internally they are blackened by organic material, but they have a white outside crust. If you break a flint across you will notice it has a conchoidal (shell-like) fracture: the new surfaces are curved very gently, something like the inside of an oyster-shell.

The smaller rusty-looking nodules you find in chalk—sometimes called "thunderbolts"—are marcasite, a form of iron ore. Its brown surface consists of iron rust and, though if you break it open it looks very bright and seems to be arranged in needles, it soon rusts and loses all its attractiveness.

Rocks from Hardened Wood

Coal is another sedimentary rock, for it was formed under water; it may be stratified and it contains many fossils—most of these are the remains not of animals but of plants, the swamp-forests which grew ages ago.

Decaying plants mingled with soil may turn into peat, a rather poor-quality fuel. Later they may become a stony material which still shows traces of a woody structure; this is brown coal, also called lignite, from the Latin for wood.

In the various types of coal the plants are much more completely converted into mineral. In bituminous coal, the ordinary household fuel, which is so soft that it soils everything it touches, you may sometimes see the imprints of fossil tree-bark or leaves or roots; under the micro-scope other traces of plant structure are visible. The hard anthracite, valued as a boiler fuel, is so completely mineralised you would not expect to find any fossils in it.

Rocks from Salt

There are regions in Cheshire where you bygone seas, is very different from purified table salt. In its natural state it is very hard. Some of it is colourless or white but most of it stained yellow or red with iron and other impurities.

In Central Europe there are great beds of rock-salt thousands of feet thick. It also occurs in bulk in India, Australia and the United States: near the Gulf of Mexico there are great salt-domes which

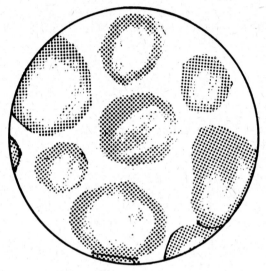

FIGURE 4. *Wind-blown sand grains, polished and rounded by friction with the rocks and with one another*

would be surprised to see houses leaning askew and braced together with iron clamps, and you would also notice a number of flashes, or shallow pools. You might think that there had been an earth-quake here or a number of air-raids, but this strange landscape is really due to the salt-mining.

In those districts there are large masses of underground rock-salt: some of it is mined away, while some is obtained more easily by pumping fresh water into the ground and pumping it out again as brine. So much of the salt has been removed that the ground above it has simply caved in.

Rock-salt, formed by the drying up of seem to have been thrust up from within the earth. Around low-lying stretches of water with no outlet to the sea, like the Great Salt Lake of Utah and the Dead Sea, rock-salt is still being formed.

Ironstone

There are several different ores of iron; some of them are sedimentary rocks. In the sand-hills of south-east England there are thin irregular sheets of "iron pan" looking something like plates of rusty iron, as well as larger nodules, which at one time were systematically worked as a source of iron. Elsewhere are much larger beds of ironstone which are still being worked: some of them have an oolitic structure, being formed of small grains firmly cemented together.

Rocks Formed by the Wind

There are other rocks which, though they did not accumulate under water, nevertheless resemble the sedimentary ones. Although they were formed on dry land, they are stratified. Wind-blown sand may pile up behind the beaches, as sand-dunes, and may be driven further inland by gales. These moving dunes may be high enough to bury great buildings and large enough to block river-mouths and cause flooding but, fortunately, they can be bound and stabilised by plants, like the marram-grass, which find nourishment even in sand.

Unusual in the British Isles but forming large tracts of rock in other parts of the world are masses of wind-blown dust called loess. Consisting mostly of grains of clay, the dust is solidified by the water that seeps into it and by its own weight. At last, it settles down so firmly that, in China, whole villages have been excavated into it. Loess also occurs in Central Asia and in the valleys of the Rhine, the Danube and the Mississippi.

The Rocks' Origin

Apart from their fossils and any other organic material they contain, all sedimentary rocks, from the coarsest pudding-stone to the finest-grained silt-stone or the loess, are formed from the remains of older rocks. The pebbles in some of the conglomerates consist of sandstone, whose grains must have come from older rocks still.

Where did these older rocks come from, and how were they formed?

CHAPTER III

Rocks Formed by Molten Material

MANY ROCKS are unstratified and are not formed of fragments cemented together. Some plainly consist of crystals of different minerals firmly interlocked together, and the microscope shows that others are similarly formed of mineral crystals too small to be visible to the unaided eye. The fragments of these rocks, piled up and hardened, produced the sedimentary rocks.

Rocks Emitted by Volcanoes

It is easy to see where some of them come from: they are erupted from volcanoes and they consist of intensely hot material, a magma, from deep within the earth. These volcanic rocks, as you would expect, are very different from the sedimentary ones, though some of them are stratified and others even contain fossils. All rocks of this type, formed by the cooling down of a molten magma, are called igneous (fire-formed) rocks.

Newly-formed volcanoes have been watched, and photographed, right from their very start. A hole, the volcanic vent, opens in the ground and emits clouds of steam and gas, streams of a molten rock, lava, and showers of solid material ranging from a very fine volcanic ash to the so-called volcanic bombs, lumps of lava glowing hot and smoking as they hurtle through the air. Some of the ash falls round the vent, and there, inter-bedded with sheets of cooled lava, it piles up to form a conical hill with a crater at its summit. Bubbles of gas in the cooling lava turn it into the porous stone, pumice.

The ash from a really violent explosion may be carried far away by the wind. That emitted in 1883 by Krakatoa, a volcano in the East Indies, stayed in the air for years. Before it dispersed it travelled several times round the earth.

When ash falls into the sea, or into lakes or rivers, it sinks to their floor, and when buried under later sediments may harden into a solid rock, tuff. Larger fragments of material from a volcano similarly produce a rock something like a breccia but called a volcanic agglomerate. These rocks may contain fossils of the creatures which the ash or other material buried as it sank through the water.

Volcanoes have also opened under the sea. The material they emitted, cooled by the water, piled up until it reached the surface, forming a new island. Some of the material from these submarine erup-tions, mixed with the sediment which was being deposited at the same time, has produced hardened lava-flows and layers of volcanic ash interbedded with the sedimentary rocks.

A volcano may die down and become dormant or extinct. Then the lava in and below its crater solidifies into a plug of very hard rock. When a dormant volcano again becomes active this plug may be too hard for the molten lava to dislodge; so the lava has to find a different way to the surface and form another crater some dis-tance from the first.

After a volcano has become completely

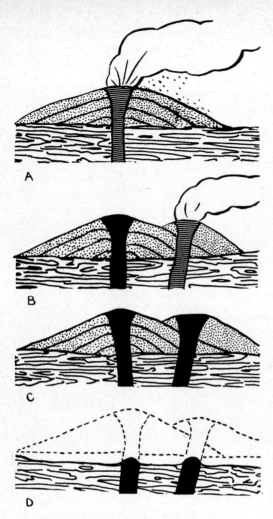

FIGURE 5. *The history of an extinct volcano*

A. *A volcanic vent opens and throws out lava and ash which pile up to form a conical hill*

B. *The lava cools and plugs the vent with a solid mass of stone. Another vent opens nearby*

C. *The volcano becomes extinct and consists of two hills of ash and lava round a central plug*

D. *The hills are destroyed by the weather and only part of the plug remains, forming two volcanic necks*

extinct, the loose material which forms its cone weathers away more quickly than these plugs of hardened lava. They then remain projecting above the ground as

volcanic necks, rounded hills of an unusual shape.

Though there are now no active volcanoes in Britain, many of its rocks were produced by volcanic action. Some of its hills and mountain ridges are the remains of cooled lava flows, and Snowdon itself consists largely of volcanic rocks, its summit being a fossiliferous volcanic ash.

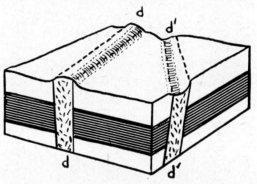

FIGURE 6. *Model illustrating dykes—if they are harder than the stratified rocks beside them, they stand out as a ridge (D–D). If they are softer, they form a groove (D′–D′)*

Some of the best-known hills in the Scottish Lowlands are volcanic necks: Arthur's Seat and the Castle Hill of Edinburgh; Dumbarton Castle rock in the Firth of Clyde; and North Berwick Law in Haddingtonshire. The *Puys* of Central France are steep-sided volcanic necks towering over the surrounding plain; one, which rises almost vertically, is nearly three hundred feet high, and another, not quite so steep, over four hundred feet.

Rocks Formed Near the Surface

Interbedded among the ordinary sedimentary strata you may find a layer of rock of a very different type, it may even "change its horizon" by passing through another bed and continuing with the same dip as before but at a different level. In other places the same type of rock forms great slabs, upright or nearly so, cutting right through all the sedimentary strata and possibly standing out above the surface of the ground like a wall.

This rock, basalt, also called whinstone

he found, the more like basalt it became; true, it did not look exactly like basalt, but the difference was solely due to the action of the weather on its surface.

Bedding and cleavage in slate—Cayton Slate Quarry, Cornwall

and trap (from a Scandinavian word meaning "stair"), is very hard, very dark, and, except for a few large mineral crystals, very fine-grained. The microscope shows that it is formed not like siltstone, of grains cemented together, but of a multitude of very fine tightly-interlocked crystals, consisting of several very complicated compounds of silica.

The naturalists did not know what to make of basalt until it was investigated in the eighteenth century by the French geologist Nicholas Desmarest. While studying the extinct volcanoes of Central France he traced a great lava-flow right across country from the former crater where it began. The further it had gone,

Lava-flows, Dykes and Sills

Basalt is, in fact, an igneous rock-like lava, but it did not all come from the ordinary volcanic vents. Some was produced by fissure eruptions, when the ground split open in long crevices and emitted rivers of lava, many miles wide, which have now hardened into rock.

Not all the molten material welling up from within the earth reached the surface. Some of it forced its way vertically upwards through the joints in the rock and, in doing so, it cooled into basalt. Now that the softer rocks alongside it have weathered away, some of the hard lava may be left as a wall-like ridge. Such a vertical sheet of basalt is called a dyke.

Columnar jointing in basalt—the Giant's Causeway, Northern Ireland

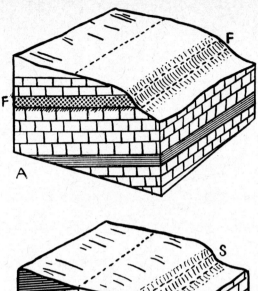

FIGURE 7. *Lava flows and sills (model)*

A. *Lava flow (F–F) running parallel with bedding and slightly baking the rocks below*

B. *Sill, (S–S) changing its horizon and baking the rocks above and below*

Some of the molten material did not get as far as the surface but forced its way in between two layers of stratified rock. There it hardened, forming a sheet of basalt interbedded with the sedimentary rock, a sill.

A sill looks rather like an ancient lava flow, but there are ways of distinguishing them:

Lava flow
May have volcanic tuffs above or below.

Its heat has slightly metamorphosed only the rock below it.

A little of the basalt forms small veins in rocks below.

Its interior is "slaggy".

Never changes its horizon.

Sill
No volcanic tuffs.

Considerable metamorphism both above and below.

The basalt has sent larger veins into the rocks above and below.

Interior coarsely crystalline.

May change its horizon, by passing through another layer of rock and continuing on the other side.

Basalt Scenery

So hard a rock, standing out boldly after the softer rocks nearby have been destroyed by the weather, naturally forms striking scenery, especially where it has contracted in cooling into a number of stone prisms perpendicular to its surface. In dykes, these prisms are quite small and lie horizontally; in lava flows and sills they are quite large and stand almost upright. On the island of Staffa, off the Scottish coast, and the Giant's Causeway, on the coast of Northern Ireland, the cooling basalt formed stone columns, most of them six-sided; they are up to two feet across, and some are about two hundred feet tall.

Some of the great ridges formed by the basalt extend across country for miles. In Yorkshire, the Cleveland Dyke is about eighty miles long; the Great Whin sill is about a hundred miles, and so steep-sided is the ridge it forms that the Emperor Hadrian used it as a foundation for the Roman Wall he erected to defend England against the Scots in about A.D. 122. Even larger is the Palisade Trap of New Jersey, in the United States, which covers an area of 6,000 square miles and, in places, is 850 feet thick.

A dyke on a raised beach at Loch Tabart, Argyll, Scotland

Part of the Great Whin Sill

Mural jointing in Dartmoor granite

Rocks Formed Deep Underground

Another well-known rock also aroused many arguments; this is granite (named from the Italian for grains). It is very hard and resistant to the weather. It forms many outcrops in Britain, and it is so abundant on the Atlantic coast of North America that New Hampshire is called the Granite State.

In granite you can distinguish the crystals of at least three different minerals: the white or red crystals which give the rock its colour are felspar; the black flakes which gleam as they catch the light are mica; and the grey, glassy material is quartz. Among the largish crystals which line some of the holes in the granite you may find the "semi-precious" stones topaz and beryl. All these minerals, except the quartz which consists of silica, are combinations of silica with aluminium and other elements.

The Origin of Granite

In the eighteenth century there was one widely-accepted explanation of granite, for the German mineralogist who put it forward, Abraham Werner, had a great reputation. (And no wonder, for like Axel, in Jules Verne's *Journey to the Centre of the Earth*, he had been used to geological specimens from early childhood.) He believed that granite, and also basalt and most other rocks, had been formed as a sort of chemical sludge at the bottom of an immense ocean which had once covered the whole earth.

Another contemporary geologist, James Hutton, took a very different view, believing that, like basalt, granite had been formed by the cooling down of a molten magma. Bitter arguments broke out between the "Neptunists" who supported Werner and the "Vulcanists" and "Plutonists" who supported Hutton. At last the dispute was settled. Though it is still not clear exactly how granite was formed, it is mostly an igneous rock.

In recent years, however, it has been realised that some granites have been formed by the alteration of sedimentary rocks, or of other igneous rocks, caused by the circulation of hot fluids rising from deep in the earth's crust. They may show signs of their sedimentary origin, consisting of alternate strata of altered sandstone and other types of rock.

One argument the "Neptunists" used was that when molten material cools down it becomes not ordinary rock but a glassy substance. This was difficult to answer until another Scots geologist, James Hall, happened to visit a glass-works where some molten glass had accidentally been cooled slowly instead of quickly. He found that it had changed into a white opaque mass formed of many tiny crystals. When this was remelted and cooled quickly it became ordinary glass. Plainly, whenever a molten material cools, the sort of substance it turns into depends upon the time the process takes.

Hall later became the first great experimental geologist. Taking specimens of various rocks into an iron foundry, he had them melted down in its furnace; when they cooled quickly they formed a glassy substance something like the rock obsidian, but when this was again melted and cooled very slowly it produced a rock-like material. When you "grow" crystals from a chemical solution their size depends on the time they take to form; Hall had shown that this is also true when a molten material cools down.

Two volcanic necks of Le Puy. The one in the foreground is 280 feet high; the church on its summit dates from the tenth century. On the more distant peak, which is 435 feet high, is a statue of the Virgin and Child

In lava flows and dykes and sills, most of which are not very thick, the molten magma was quickly chilled by the air or the rocks which touched it, so that it formed basalt, whose crystals are microscopically small. The size of the crystals in granite show that it welled up in quantities too large to cool rapidly, and was sheltered from the chill air by a great thickness of rock. It never reached the surface; instead, it forced the over-lying rocks upwards like a great blister, and cooled beneath them, forming a granite boss. The rocks which formerly covered it have now been destroyed by the weather, as has part of the granite itself.

Granite Scenery

Granite produces moorland country: the whole of Dartmoor covers one large boss; Land's End is another, the sea having worn much of it away; and there are others at Shap Fell in Westmorland, in the Lleyn peninsula of North Wales, and in the Scottish Highlands. Their weather-worn surfaces produce the granite tors and many of these show mural jointing, looking something like masonry.

To distinguish them from the volcanic rocks, which were poured out on the surface, rocks formed deep in the earth, like granite, are classed as the plutonic rocks, Pluto being, in ancient times, the god of the underworld.

Transformed Rocks

One of the "Neptunist's" chief arguments was that intense heat does not produce rocks but destroys them; heated limestone, for example, gives off its carbon dioxide and is converted into lime. But Hall proved that this happens only when it is heated in the open air; by heating limestone or chalk in sealed iron tubes, he changed them into another well-known rock, marble.

Marble, an ornamental white rock consisting of crystallised calcite, is one of the metamorphic rocks whose whole structure has been transformed by intense heat or pressure.

Gneiss contains much the same minerals as granite, and perhaps it used to be granite, but it looks quite different: its minerals have been forced by earth movements into irregular curved layers, giving it a banded appearance. You may find in it small dark red crystals of a newly-formed mineral, garnet (another of the many compounds of silica).

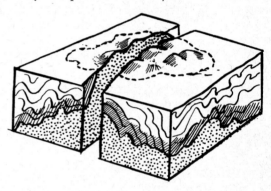

FIGURE 8. *Model illustrating granite boss, metamorphosing the rocks which surround it*

In schist the minerals form very thin flakes, which you can split away quite easily—they may be reminiscent of the flakes of puff pastry. Some of the mica-schists, which you can recognise by the sheen of the mica, are metamorphosed clays.

When you look at slate you may find that it is marked by parallel streaks rather like the layers in a sedimentary rock, but that some of them are bent into folds. When you split the slate, however, you may find that it cleaves (splits) not parallel to these layers but across them. It was originally a shale, but powerful pressures within the earth have altered its structure, so that it now splits in a direction different from that of the pressure. Any fossils it contains look queerly distorted, the pressure which metamorphosed the rock having wrenched them out of shape.

Many great granite bosses are surrounded by a broad metamorphic aureole (halo). In this, the rocks have been so completely transformed by the heat from the molten granite that new minerals have formed in them, and they are also traversed by veins of igneous rock.

These igneous and metamorphic rocks are the ones from whose fragments the sedimentary rocks were formed: in a conglomerate you may, for example, be able to recognise pebbles of granite or basalt. Most sandstones consist of grains of quartz, though there are micaceous sandstones in which many of the grains, as you will see from their glitter, are specks of mica. These grains and specks come from granite bosses destroyed by the weather, under whose action the felspar softens and turns into the white china clay.

Sedimentary rocks were all formed from the remains of igneous rocks. So, too, were the metamorphic rocks, and many of these were transformed by contact with the igneous rocks. The igneous rocks, however, do not consist of fragments of other rocks, but of cooled-down molten material. But where did this molten material come from and how was it formed?

CHAPTER IV

Within the Earth

To UNDERSTAND where the molten material came from we have to know something about the earth's interior.

This knowledge is very hard to obtain, for the deepest mines and boreholes go down only a very short distance compared with the earth's diameter. Ingenious methods have, however, been invented for ascertaining conditions deep underground: one of them is to time the shock-waves which earthquakes send in all directions right through the earth. This work is part of another science, geophysics.

The Earth's Internal Heat

The interior of the earth must certainly be intensely hot. Even in mines, though they do not go very deep, the temperature increases at about 100 degrees for every mile. The heat is shown, too, not only by volcanoes of molten lava but also by geysers which squirt out jets of boiling water and steam, fumeroles which emit clouds of steam and other gases, and hot springs, whose water is not only warm but full of chemicals. Britain has neither fumeroles or geysers, and only one hot spring, but this is so famous for the medicinal value of its water that it gave a name to the city of Bath.

There are many fumeroles and geysers in other lands. The word *geyser* is Icelandic in origin, and that country, as you would expect, is famous for them. There are many geysers, too, in New Zealand, South Africa and Malaya. The scenery in the Yellowstone National Park of Wyoming is so amazing that the trapper who discovered it early in the nineteenth century found that nobody would believe him: in addition to magnificent geysers it contains boiling springs and petrified forests, and its rocks are brilliantly coloured by chemicals brought up by the springs.

The Structure of the Earth

The methods used by the geophysicists show that around the earth's centre is a core, about four thousand miles across, of nickel-steel, but what sort of condition it is in, whether it is solid, or liquid, or even a highly-compressed gas, we do not know. We have no experience of materials exposed to temperatures and pressures which are so very great, and pressure, like temperature, increases with the depth.

What comes next is uncertain, but it seems likely that for some distance the nickel-steel from the central core blends with the rock olivine. Beyond this is a layer, nearly two thousand miles thick, of the olivine itself; it is a heavy, greenish rock, a compound of silica with magnesium and iron.

The upper surface of the olivine sphere is about fifty miles below the surface and is surrounded by the more ordinary rocks. Immediately above it is a thick layer of basalt; on top of this is a thinner layer of granite, part of it, covered by the sedimentary rocks, forms the earth's land masses.

The interesting thing is that the basalt is believed to be so very hot that it is not

The hot spring of Hveragerdi, Iceland

A crater of boiling magma at Pozzuoli, Naples

solid but plastic, acting in much the same way as a sluggish liquid such as thick treacle. The granite is near enough to the surface to be solid and, as it is somewhat lighter than basalt, it floats like a stone raft, partly submerged in the treacly basalt. It may remain motionless, or it may drift very slowly across the basalt—indeed, some geophysicists think that great masses of granite, with the sedimentary rocks upon them, have drifted for long distances about the earth.

Continental Drift

When you look at a world map or a globe of the earth you cannot help seeing that the two shores of the Atlantic seem to be almost parallel. Off northern America, too, the coast of Greenland seems parallel with that of Labrador, and the islands nearby look almost like the separated pieces of a jigsaw puzzle. You can well imagine that these lands were once joined together but were somehow split asunder and drifted apart.

The theory of continental drift, worked out early this century by the German geologist Alfred Wegener, is that long ago all the southern continents formed a huge land mass round the South Pole. Earth movements made this split, so that South America, Africa, India, and Australia broke off and began drifting away. During their slow motion across the basalt "sea", smaller tracts of land broke away from them and lagged behind, forming such islands as Tasmania, Ceylon and Madagascar.

Further north was an even greater land mass. This also split, North America breaking loose from Europe and drifting westwards; later its north-eastern part split off and become Greenland and the adjacent islands. When the two Americas met, they merged together and continued their western drift, meantime shedding a number of small islands in the Caribbean Sea and elsewhere.

Australia moved more slowly than Africa and India, which drifted on until they collided with the Eurasian land mass to their north. Although they were moving slowly, the impact of the collision was so great that it produced powerful earth movements. These contorted the solid rock into folds, raising such great mountain masses as the Himalayas and the Alps and also producing the more gentle foldings of south-eastern England.

Later, another split detached Africa from Arabia, and opened a great rift which extends from the Jordan Valley down the Red Sea and southwards through Africa, about one sixth of the way round the earth. Nor have the earth movements yet ceased, for there is some evidence that Greenland is still drifting very slowly westwards.

Strange as this theory is, many geologists take it seriously, so well does it explain the layout of sea and land. It is confirmed by a study of the earth's magnetic forces.

It was probably radio-activity in the rocks which sent these immense land masses drifting about the earth.

How did the Earth Begin?

You will see that there is one further question to consider: however its rocks were formed and whatever its structure may be, how did the earth begin? This is not a geological matter, it is a problem for the astronomers, and they have made some very interesting attempts to solve it.

A recent theory is that the earth was originally part of one of the two suns which formed a double star. This sun, it is thought, exploded, and became a cloud of incandescent gas revolving about its companion, which is now our sun. The gas, as it cooled, gradually formed spheres,

Yellowstone Park: in the foreground are pools of hot water shut in by terraces formed by minerals from the springs. In the background geysers may be seen spouting

Geysers in Yellowstone Park.   The one in the foreground is called the Whirligig Geyser

and these became the planets and our own earth.

The gas cloud which produced our earth cooled still further and became a sphere of intensely hot liquid, consisting of molten rocks which sorted themselves out, roughly in order of weight.   The heavy nickel-steel sank towards the centre, with the olivine around it; outside this was a molten magma which at last cooled enough to form solid rock, but this remelted and formed again many times before it was so cool that it could remain permanently solid.

In some such way the rocks of which the earth is made were formed.   By studying them, the geologist seeks to trace the history of our world and of its plants and animal inhabitants.   To understand his methods we have first to realise how every-day processes can transform the surface rocks into scenery and produce the varied landscape of ancient times and the present day.

CHAPTER V

Earth Movements

Whether they are sedimentary and consist of the fragments of older rocks or are igneous and formed from a cooled magma, almost all rocks began below the sea or deep underground. But how did they ever come to the surface? And why do we find the remains of plants and animals transformed into stones buried in many of them?

The Theory of Sudden Disasters

The early geologists puzzled over such problems and found a simple answer. Believing that every word of the Bible is *literally* true, they thought that the earth had been created, more or less as it is now, a few thousand years ago, and that it had been swamped by Noah's Flood. This great deluge which, the Bible told them, had risen above the loftiest mountains, seemed quite powerful enough to have worn from the land the sediment which forms so many of the rocks and to have buried within them the bodies of the creatures which its waters had drowned.

But the rocks, especially in the mountains, look as if they had been affected by something far more violent than a flood. They seem piled up in utter confusion; some, though now on the mountain tops, were plainly formed beneath the sea; some have been tilted, bent, crumpled, snapped, thrust one over another, smashed and rent out of shape. So, it was thought, the flood must have been accompanied by raging tempests, violent earthquakes and volcanic outbreaks. At last, the tumult must have ceased and the waters subsided, leaving the earth much as we see it today.

Then it was seen that one such disaster, however vast, could not account for everything. Some rock-beds lie almost horizontally across the edges of others, though both are formed of hardened silt and both contain fossils. Noah's Flood might possibly explain how the upper strata had been formed, but what about the lower ones?

The geologists, who now realised that the earth was far older than a few thousand years, believed that there had been not one great catastrophe but several. They thought that the earth had been convulsed by fierce gales and torrential rains, by volcanic eruptions and earthquakes, not once, but time and again.

Surely, too, they thought, each of these disasters must have killed off every living thing on earth and, later, new types of animals and plants had been created to people the world afresh. After each of the disasters the earth seemed to have been fairly peaceful—until the next. Such was the theory, called catastrophism, which many geologists held up to about a century and half ago. One of them even thought that all the living creatures had been destroyed, and new ones created, twenty-seven separate times!

The Theory of Gradual Change

This did not sound very likely and, in 1783, the Scots geologist James Hutton suggested something very different. He

Submerged forest and (in distance) peat-bog—Freshwater Bay, Pembrokeshire

believed that the earth's many changes were due not to sudden disasters separated by long periods of quiet but to the piled-up effect of much slower and more gradual processes; this theory is called uniformitarianism. Then, of course, came the problem of exactly what these processes were. Long and bitter were the disputes between the "catastrophists" who believed in the sudden disasters and the "uniformitarians" who did not.

The Father of Modern Geology

The dispute was still at its height when, early in the nineteenth century, the young geologist Charles Lyell saw that newly-formed bed of freshwater limestone. He had seen, too, the damage which the sea had done on the Norfolk coast, and the new land it had formed by depositing silt at Romney Marsh. So, like Hutton, he was convinced that the earth has reached its present state not through sudden disasters but through the quiet age-long action of everyday forces—the very forces which are at work around us now.

Lyell devoted his life to geology. His work took him far over the earth. In 1830, he published the first volume of a splendid book, *The Principles of Geology*, which was, he said, "an attempt to explain the changes of the earth's surface by reference to causes now in operation." His attempt was so successful that, though it did not end the arguments at once, it settled the dispute about the earth's history.

His book explained that though there have been serious floods and other catastrophies, none has been violent enough to convulse the whole earth and destroy all its living creatures. He placed the science of geology on a sound basis. "We collect the facts," said another geologist, "and he teaches us to understand them." But this is hardly fair to Lyell, who collected quite a number of facts himself. He has been called "the Father of Modern Geology".

Much has been learned since Lyell's time. New discoveries have been made, new methods devised for making them. And the work is still going on, not only in newly-explored lands but everywhere. Mining and quarrying, and the excavations made for new buildings and roads, bring into sight rocks which have never before been visible.

Earth Movements

You can see for yourself how everyday forces are destroying the earth: the weather is wearing away its surface, the rivers are trenching it with valleys, the sea is nibbling away its coasts. You can see, too, how new land is formed, where the rivers deposit their silt in the estuaries and where the sea piles up sand and gravel along the shore. But these processes, left to themselves, would end by reducing all the earth to a flattish plain, hardly above sea-level. Is there anything to counteract them? Is there any force that could actually raise the whole level of the land?

Lyell found that there is. He knew that a Swedish scientist, Celsius, hearing some fishermen say that during their lifetime some rocks had risen above the water, had put a mark exactly at sea level on a rock near Stockholm. But when Lyell visited that rock a century later, he found that the mark was about thirty inches above sea level; so in that region the sea-floor was rising. On the mainland, too, there were layers of fossil shellfish at different levels up to hundreds of feet above the water. The movement had plainly been going on for some time.

In many other places the earth is slowly rising, but elsewhere it is sinking. In some parts of the world there is clear evidence

A drowned valley—the River Dart, Devon

of one or both of these movements, or of changes in the level of the sea itself.

Lands Sunk Below the Sea

The river mouths in the west country of England look very different from the usual estuaries. The rivers and their tributaries flow not through wide valleys floored by level stretches of silt but through narrow, winding creeks between tree-clad banks which slope steeply down to high-water mark. These creeks used to be ordinary inland rivers, but the whole of that part of the land sank and the valleys were invaded by the sea.

The Fal and the Tamar are examples of these drowned valleys; Milford Haven is another; and there are many others along the coasts of south-west Ireland, west Scotland, Norway and Iceland. Off the west coast of Alaska are a number of islands; these were formerly hills but, as the land sank, the sea flowed in behind them and separated them from the mainland.

On many beaches the ebbing tide discloses tree-trunks partly buried in the sand. These submerged forests may be seen off Swansea Bay and elsewhere in the Bristol Channel, in the Mersey Estuary, and in Torbay. Near Penzance is St. Michael's Mount, whose name in the Cornish language means "the venerable rock within the woods"; but those woods are now buried beneath the silt of Mount's Bay; what was once a rock in the woodlands has become an island cut off from the shore except at low tide. Off some shores, too, there are submerged peat bogs covered by the sand.

This makes us wonder what truth there is in the old legends about broad tracts of country which have sunk bodily beneath the sea. Off the coast of Cardigan Bay is said to be the Lost Hundred, once a stretch of fertile countryside; and there is a tradition that north and west of Cornwall was a great forest in which King Arthur and his knights and ladies used to hunt. But both these regions are now covered by the waves, except that the hill-tops of the Lost Land of Lyonesse may still project above the water as the Scilly Isles.

Lands Risen Above the Sea

Though parts of the coast have sunk, others have risen. You know what a sea-beach looks like, with its stretch of sand,

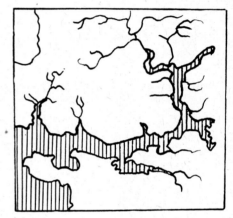

FIGURE 9. *Drowned valley—Milford Haven, Pembrokeshire*

gravel or rock sloping down from the cliff-foot to the sea. You might be surprised to find what is plainly a beach some distance above sea level, sloping down gently from the foot of one cliff to the crest of another. There are many raised beaches along the British shores; in some places, indeed, there are two series of them, about twenty-five and fifty feet, respectively, above sea level; and along part of the coast of Cornwall and Anglesey are much wider wave-cut platforms, several hundred feet above the sea.

Raised beaches have been found in regions as far distant as Greenland, New Zealand and the White Sea. In South

St. Michael's Mount, Cornwall

America they extend along the coast, from Tierra del Fuego northward, for about two thousand miles, and much of the east coast of the United States is a raised sea-floor which stretches some way inland to the Fall Line, a former sea-coast from which the rivers descend in rapids and waterfalls.

Lands Sunken *and* Risen

There are places where the land shows that it sank beneath the sea and afterwards rose above it. On the top of the cliffs east of Lulworth Cove is the Fossil Forest, a number of tree-trunks transformed into stone. One of the petrified trees in the grounds of the Natural History Museum at South Kensington came from a Fossil

Grove in the Victoria Park, Glasgow. These, however, are small compared with the Petrified Forest of Adamana, Arizona, where some of the fossil tree-trunks are up to 200 feet long. The trees in all these forests grow above sea level—some of them are types which flourish away from the coast—to get "petrified" they had to sink below it, and now they are once again on dry land.

Such movements took place long ago, but others have happened within historic times. On the Italian coast, near Naples, are some ancient ruins: they include two pavements, one just below sea level, the other a little lower. On the upper pavement stand three columns, and about half-way along their length these are pierced

The so-called Temple of Serapis *at Pozzuoli, Naples.   The dark markings just above water level on the columns are borings made by marine animals*

A section of Coral on the Great Barrier Reef

with holes bored by marine animals. Their position shows that since the lower pavement was laid, at or above sea level, the coast has sunk at least twenty-five feet and had since risen about twenty feet.

Coral Islands and Reefs

Coral consists of the calcite "skeletons" of countless tiny animals something like sea-anemones. In tropical seas, it may form a coral island or atoll, a circle enclosing a lagoon; a fringing reef extending outwards from the land; or a barrier reef further out to sea and parallel with the shore. In 1770, Captain Cook discovered the great Barrier Reef off eastern Australia by the painful process of running his ship on it.

As the coral animals can live only at, or

a little below, sea level and as some reefs extend much further down, it is hard to explain how the reefs were formed. Darwin, who studied them during his voyage on the exploring ship *Beagle*, thought that when the reefs were built the sea-floor was slowly sinking.

At first, when it was still above sea level, the coral would form a fringing reef round it; as the land sank, the distance between shore and reef would increase and, as the reef was built higher—at the new sea level —it would become a barrier reef; and finally, when all the land had sunk, the reef—still being built higher—would become an atoll. Throughout the whole process the animals would use the coral already formed as a basis on which to build.

41

A raised beach—Manorbier, Pembrokeshire

Other theories have been suggested and it is not yet certain which is right. But the great thickness of the reefs, whose base is far below the level at which the animals can live, shows that some movement of the sea-floor must have taken place. Deep borings made recently in the atolls suggest that Darwin's theory was correct.

CHAPTER VI

The Build of the Rocks

WHATEVER THE rocks are, their structure—their order and their build underground—has a great effect on the scenery and on what happens to the rocks themselves when they are exposed on the surface. The geologist tries to recognise, from surface indications, what sort of rocks are below and what their structure is.

Order of Superposition

The sedimentary rocks were formed by material that accumulated on the sea-floor; its upper layers were, of course, deposited after those beneath them. For this reason, since the sediment hardened to become solid rock and rose to form dry land, its upper strata are almost everywhere more recent than the ones below. There are exceptions, but these are easy to recognise: the whole series of strata may have been inverted by earth movements, bringing the more recent rocks to the top; or, as in a sill, a sheet of magma may have been forced between two sedimentary beds, so that it is more recent than some of the rocks above it. Usually, however, the order of superposition of the rocks— their arrangement one above another—

Syncline and anticline—Wrangle Point, Bude, Cornwall

shows the order in which they were formed.

Folding

As it accumulated on the sea-floor, the sediment formed layers which were either horizontal or sloped very gently, parallel

Where the beds dip more steeply there is less difference between the two slopes.

Some rock formations are so common, and so important, that they have special names. In an anticline the rock-beds dip away from a central line; in a syncline they dip towards it. Beds dipping in-

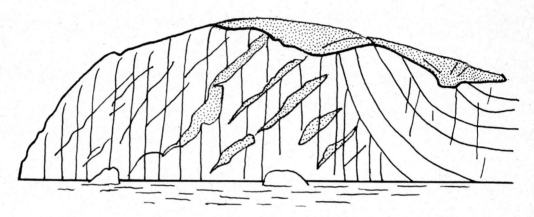

FIGURE 10. *Junction of vertical and curved strata in chalk—Ballard Head, Dorset*

to the surface below them. As these layers, now hardened into solid rock, were lifted by earth movements to form dry land, some were simply raised without being tilted and are still almost horizontal, as are the blue lias cliffs east of Lyme Regis and the rocks cut into by the Niagara Falls. Some were tilted as they rose and still dip, more or less steeply. Some are almost vertical: in the cliffs of Marloes Bay, Pembrokeshire, for example, are the Three Chimneys, three parallel beds of very dark quarzite standing on end in the cliff face. Some have been turned bodily upside-down.

A gently-sloping bed of hard rock overlying softer rocks forms an escarpment, a prominent ridge, such as the Cotswold Hills. On one side, the dip slope, the ground slopes as gently as the rocks that form it; on the other, the scarp, it is much steeper and may even form an inland cliff.

wards in all directions towards a central point form a basin; those dipping outwards form a dome. In a pitching anticline or syncline the whole formation is tilted along its central line. In a monocline or "hogback" the beds, after dipping gently downwards, tilt upwards very steeply and then dip gently as before but at a different level.

In south-east England the chalk dips down from the Chilterns under the Thames and up again in the North Downs, forming the London Syncline, sometimes wrongly called the London Basin. Beyond the North Downs, the strata below the chalk form the Wealden Anticline, vanishing beneath the South Downs. The vertical beds of chalk which form the "backbone" of the Isle of Wight are part of a monocline, and there are many monoclines in the western part of North America. The rocks around Harlech, in

North Wales, form a dome, and those in the South Wales and Forest of Dean coalfields form basins.

You might expect the syncline to form valleys and the anticlines to form hills; so, in some places, they do. This is exceptional, however, for the movements which produced these formations stretched the rocks at the top of the anticline and split

large enough to form whole mountain ranges. Rock-beds may even be doubled back over themselves in an overfold, as in the Alps, so that masses of the rock are upside-down.

James Hall, the Scots geologist (1761-1832), devised an experiment to show how these contortions in the strata were produced. Placing a number of layers of

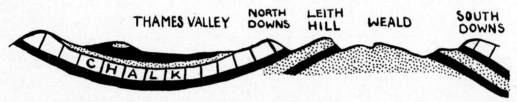

FIGURE 11. *Rocks near London. A simplified section showing the Thames syncline and the Wealden anticline (the beds marked in black are clays)*

them into fragments, thus reducing their resistance to the weather. They compressed and hardened the rocks in the upper part of the synclines and so made them more resistant. The chalk formerly extended right across the Weald from the North Downs to the South and, had it not been destroyed, it would have formed a hill over a thousand feet high; but the

cloth on a flat surface, he weighed them down and then pressed their two ends towards one another. This folded and crumpled the cloth, making it look very like the contorted strata in the rocks.

It was at one time thought that these contortions were evidence of violent catastrophies which had suddenly crumpled the strata. But rocks, when they are violently

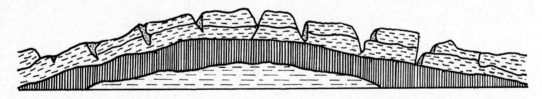

FIGURE 12. *How the rocks in an anticline are stretched apart and weakened*

movements which raised this chalk weakened it so much that the weather destroyed it even as it rose.

Contorted Strata

In some places the rock-beds have not merely been bent but have been folded and crumpled together. Such contorted strata may be quite small, as in Stair Hole near Lulworth in Dorset, or they may be

compressed, do not bend, but simply break up into fragments. To throw them into contortions without breaking them, the earth movements must have been very gradual and have continued over a very long time.

Faulting

Some earth movements, indeed, are too violent and sudden for the rocks to resist;

instead of bending or crumpling, they break across. Such a crack in the earth's crust is called a fault; from the mining point of view that is exactly what it is.

The crack itself is called the fault plane. It is said not to dip but to hade in a given direction and at a given slope; this is

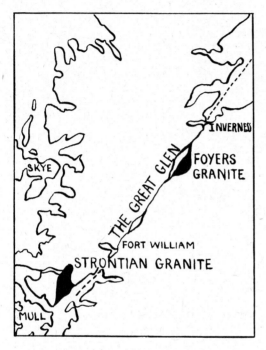

FIGURE 13. *The Great Glen fault. The two masses of granite at Strontian and Foyers are believed to have formerly been a single mass, until this was torn apart and its halves were separated by a distance of sixty-five miles by the earth movement which formed the Great Glen*

measured not from the horizontal but from the vertical. The effect of the fault is to break many rock-beds into two, and to separate the two portions, perhaps by only a few inches, perhaps by miles. The fault which produced the Great Glen of Scotland broke a granite mass into two, one portion being at the western end of the Glen, near Mull, and the other over sixty miles to its north-east, not far from Inverness.

In almost all faults the separated portions of the rock-beds are at different levels, the vertical distance between them being the fault's throw. The normal fault, the most common type, hades to the downthrow, the side on which the beds are lower; the earth movements which produce it stretched the rocks and made them snap and slide.

Except in mountainous regions, reversed faults, which hade to the upthrow, are less common; they were produced by forces which drove the ends of the rock-beds inwards, compressing them and making one portion ride up over the other. An overfold in the rocks may become an overthrust, in which one portion of the severed beds is driven bodily over the other along a thrust plane which may slope so gently it is almost horizontal.

In some districts the rocks are much faulted. The fault planes may run in different directions, cracking the strata into a crazy pavement of separate pieces. They may be parallel and hade either in the same direction, producing a step fault, or towards one another, in a trough fault.

The Great Glen of Scotland, a valley a mile wide and containing three lochs—one, Loch Ness, is in places 1,000 feet deep—is the result of a trough fault. Even larger is that in the Middle East, containing the Jordan Valley and the Dead Sea: four hundred miles long, up to twenty-five miles wide and over 2,000 feet below sea level at its deepest. The Red Sea may also be a gigantic trough fault, now flooded by the sea. Other trough faults extend southward through Africa towards the Zambesi.

There are two theories about trough faults. One is that they are the result of compression, the rocks along their sides having been thrust inwards and overridden the central part. The other is that the rocks were wrenched apart so that the central part sank bodily into the gap thus formed. Whatever its cause, the Africa trough was produced fairly recently, and

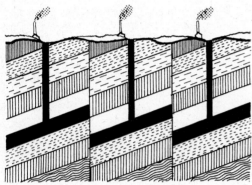

FIGURE 14. *A step fault*

the action may still be going on, for earthquakes are frequent along its line, which is marked by extinct and active volcanoes.

In parts of eastern Africa and western America there are so many faults, and these run in such varied directions, that it

Contorted strata—Hartland Quay, Devon

Faulting—Portsarn, Glamorganshire

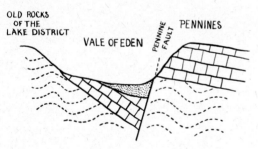

FIGURE 15. *The Pennine fault. Here a normal fault with a throw of several hundred feet has produced the Vale of Eden*

would be hard to describe them: those in a region in Arizona reminded one geologist of a shattered pane of glass. There, and in Nevada and Utah, are faults with throws of as much as two miles.

A fault may be marked by a ridge along its course, but usually this is worn away by the weather. Then the existence of the fault has to be deduced from

How faulting affects coal-mining.   Model of a section of the Haig Pit, Whitehaven

An unconformity—Helwith Bridge, Yorkshire

the outcrops of the beds affected; they may be discontinuous or doubled; or some may not appear at all.   When the fault does not extend to the surface, because new rock-beds have been formed since it occurred, it can be detected by sinking boreholes, or inferred by the pattern of surface outcrops.

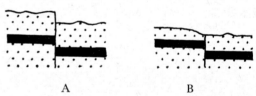

A   B

FIGURE 16.   *The development of a fault*
A.   *A fault produced this cliff on the surface*
B.   *The cliff is destroyed and the ground levelled by the weather*

Unconformities

Many rock-beds run parallel for miles, all having the same dip; the sediment which formed them must have accumulated uninterruptedly for a long period of time.   In some places, however, the rocks near the surface have a different dip from those below, and run across their upturned

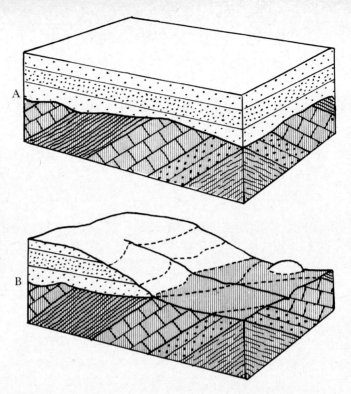

FIGURE 17. *An unconformity*

A. *The model shows how rock-beds, originally horizontal, may be lifted and tilted and their surface worn away by the weather to form hills and valleys. When they have again sunk below the sea, later rock-beds may accumulate on their surface*

B. *Effects of a second rise of the rock-beds, much of the upper series being destroyed by the weather. (The small mound is an outlier)*

edges. The surface which separates the two series of beds may be uneven, and the lowest of the upper series may be a puddingstone, containing pebbles from the rock beneath it.

Such an unconformity between the dips of the two series shows that an earth movement tilted the lower rocks before the upper ones were formed. A great unevenness in the surface which separates them shows that the lower beds were not only tilted but were raised to form dry land, and were worn into hills and valleys. Then they sank below the sea. The accumulating sediment first filled their valleys and then covered their hills. This sediment included fragments of rock worn away from them; when it hardened it produced the rock which now overlies them. A fault which cracked the lower rocks, or a dyke of igneous rock which was forced into them, may not appear in

the upper series at all, for it was produced before they were deposited. There is likely to be a great difference, too, in the types of fossils found in the rocks above and below the unconformity.

Overlap, Inliers and Outliers

When sediment is deposited on a gently-sloping sea-bed, each layer extends a little further above the slope than the one below. Later, when the sediment has become solid rock, all its beds overlap those below them.

In some places the upper rocks in a series have been worn away to expose the bed beneath them, producing an inlier. More common is the outlier, a detached portion of a rock-bed: beyond the scarp of a gently-sloping sheet of rock there may be hillocks or crags of the same material separated from the main outcrop by depressions in the ground.

E

CHAPTER VII

Weathering

About two hundred years ago the French geologist Etienne Guettard revisited the region where he was born. One of the local sights he remembered from childhood was a strangely-shaped rock that looked rather like a statue—but now, he found, it wasn't there. Moreover, in a district he knew well, he now saw other rocks which he could not remember at all. This made him realise how the weather can affect even the hardest rocks.

Changes of Temperature

By day, the warm sunshine beats down on the surface of the rocks and makes it expand a little; at night, the chill air cools it and makes it contract. These repeated changes, while the rest of the rock is unaffected, gradually loosen and crack the surface and make it flake off.

Weathering began the moment the first solid rocks were formed, for they were affected by the changes in the earth's temperature as its daily spin turned them alternately towards, and away from, the sun. That action is still going on.

Some rocks shed their surface in a series of curved layers, producing spheroidal or onion weathering; others shed it in fragments; and large pieces of rock may fall away from the face of the cliffs. The various minerals in such a rock as granite expand and contract at different rates; this too makes the surface crumble away. In desert regions, where the changes of temperature are extreme, rock faces are destroyed very rapidly. Even in regions with milder climates, the effect of temperature variation is great.

The tops of many mountains are strewn with jagged fragments shed by the rocks. On their sides are screes, slopes of rubble which have slid downhill towards the valley floor. Screes are unstable and may start sliding anew if anything—or anybody—disturbs them; a collapsing scree resembles a small avalanche. The sharp edges of the rock fragments can inflict

Results of a cloud-burst—gulley eroded by the Exmoor floods, 1952

painful or dangerous wounds, so that a scree is something to avoid.

Rainfall and Soil-creep

The rain helps the sunshine to destroy the rocks. Seeping into their joints and crannies, it expands slightly during the day and contracts during the night; it expands even more strongly when it freezes during the winter. Thus rain splits the rocks into fragments and the fragments into smaller fragments still or even into grains of dust.

The rain also washes the dust and the smaller fragments downhill, either gently as soil-creep or more violently as torrents of mud. A really heavy rainfall, or a sudden cloud-burst, can be very destructive indeed. The River Lyn, in north Devon, is normally peaceful, in summer at any rate; but in the summer of 1952 it suddenly became a raging torrent that almost destroyed Lynmouth and left the land alongside its channel strewn with masses of soil and great pieces of rock. This was caused by a sudden deluge of rain which had fallen on Exmoor, where the stream rises.

Greater rainfalls still have devastated other lands and had even more important geological results.

Even in a shower the raindrops thrust the dust grains aside or make them leap slightly into the air; on a hillside they move the grains slowly downhill. The dust works its way towards the valley like a very fine scree; it then either accumulates at the foot of the hill as a talus or falls into the stream and is swept away.

You might think it impossible for water to dissolve a rock—until you remember rock-salt! But rain, although the purest water in nature, is really a very weak solution of carbonic acid and other chemicals which it dissolves as it falls through the air. Weak though it is, the acid is strong enough to dissolve a little of the limestone and chalk. It also attacks, though more slowly, the surface of the other rocks, rusting any iron they may contain.

The Wind

The wind not only piles the sand of the sea-shore into great dunes and heaps dust together to form loess, it also helps to destroy rocks. It grinds and scrapes their

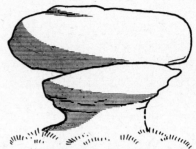

FIGURE 18. *A wind-worn rock—one of the Brimham Rocks, Yorkshire*

surface with the dust and grit it carries, acting something like sandpaper and something like a factory sand-blast.

Where a rock is uniformly hard throughout, the wind-swept dust grinds its surface smooth; some desert rocks have actually been polished by the sand carried by the wind. Where the layers that form the rock differ in hardness, the sand acts more powerfully on the soft layers and wears them into deep grooves, leaving the harder layers to project between them. The strange shape of rocks such as the Bridestones in Yorkshire is due to the action of the grit-laden wind which, in the end, will undercut their bases and make them topple over.

The Formation of Soil

Beneath the soil in your garden is a thicker layer of subsoil, where the earth has a different colour and contains scattered fragments of stone. The deeper you dig the more plentiful and the larger

Results of wind erosion—the Rocking Stones, Howden Moor, Yorkshire

these fragments are, until they are hard to distinguish from the loose surface of the rocks below; at last, you come to the rocks themselves. The whole exposure, from the top downwards, is called a soil profile.

Like the subsoil below, the soil itself may show what rocks underlie it, being sandy or clayey or containing fragments of chalk; sandy, clayey soil is called loam. Soil is very different, however, from sand-dunes or the surfaces of newly-weathered rocks; it is normally brown-coloured and rather damp.

Soil consists partly of grains worn from the rocks and partly of humus, the decaying remains of plants; it also contains living creatures, not only worms but also bacteria far too small for us to see without the aid of a microscope. This organic material fertilises the soil, so that the plants can draw nourishment from it.

The plants themselves help to produce the soil. By thrusting their roots into the crevices in the rocks they gently but firmly split them, thus making way for the chemicals in the soil to seep into them, attack them and break them up.

Even barren land where nothing will grow is converted by plants into fertile soil. Tough marram grass takes root on arid sand-dunes; the smallest particle of wind-blown soil, drifted on to a barren rock, will form a foothold for very hardy plants, and these produce more soil in which other plants can take root.

By this process, heaps of slag from a factory or rubble from a mine can be slowly transformed into pleasant grassy or tree-covered knolls. By this process, too, the face of a railway-cutting soon becomes gay with flowers.

The countless bacteria in the soil break down the remains of plants and animals into chemicals which keep it fertile. Worms, continually burrowing through it and "eating" it, help to fertilise it: they stir it up, powder and sift it, and loosen it so that the air can get at it. Charles Darwin calculated that an acre of soil may contain 50,000 earthworms who, between

Spheroidal ("onion") weathering—Latterbarrow Beck, Cumberland

A scree—Silver Cove, Beck Valley, Cumberland

The work of the Tennessee Valley Authority   (Above)   *The results of gulley erosion on the side of a hill*

(Below)   *The same hill a year and a half later after treatment by the TVA Foresters.   Trees and grass now protect the slope from further damage*

Wind erosion—the Sipapu Natural Bridge in White Canyon, Utah, USA

them, "eat" about ten tons of earth every year. But for the bacteria and the worms, there might be no soil and no plant-life; nothing but loose masses of dust and sand in which no living creature could find nourishment.

So thoroughly do the worms churn up the soil that fragments of rock may gradually get worked up to the surface. Small fossils and flint arrow-heads are also brought up, so that they are sometimes found half-buried in the soil. Such rock fragments and fossils are clues to the nature of the outcrops below.

Soil Erosion

Vegetation binds the topsoil much as marram grass binds the dunes; if it is

Grass and other plants

Soil and roots

Sub-soil with rock fragments

Solid rock

FIGURE 19. *The formation of soil*

incautiously removed the results may be disastrous. About thirty years ago, dust clouds, vast enough to darken the sky, were driven by the wind across the American prairies, over the cities and out to sea; they were due to excessive ploughing-up

55

The results of wind erosion.   A dust storm in Western Colorado: a wind of about thirty miles an hour carries loose particles of soil for hundreds of miles

Pipes in the chalk—Clayton, Suffolk

of the grasslands and destruction of the bushes and trees. This wind erosion of the newly-exposed soil gave lands which had hitherto been fertile a new and very terrible name: they had become the Dust Bowl.

Soil erosion can take other forms. Too much ploughing or large-scale forestry may cause sheet erosion when the rain washes the topsoil away bodily or gully erosion when the storm water trenches the ground into deep channels.

In ancient times, in regions from Iraq to China, the fertility of wide areas of land was destroyed in much the same manner. Some of the world's deserts may be the result of soil erosion.

Fortunately, modern Americans are able to overcome soil erosion with knowledge and appliances which no other civilisation has ever possessed. By harnessing the Tennessee River the Tennessee Valley Authority has been able to restore much of the fertility of its valley, replant forests, and so convert a backward area into a flourishing community.

Elsewhere, too, soil erosion has to be guarded against. The rain produces soil-creep on cultivated land just as it does in the wild areas, washing the surface of the ground slowly downhill. The wind can blow loose soil away. In Britain, this is prevented by what might otherwise seem a waste of good farmland, the fields being separated by hedges, stone walls, or lines of trees.

Chemicals in the Soil

Where there is little rainfall, the sun's heat first draws up the moisture in the soil and then evaporates it, leaving behind the minerals it contains. For this reason, the ground in many desert regions is saturated or covered with salt.

In such countries as Britain, where the rainfall more than makes up for the evaporation, the rain sinks into the ground, taking the minerals with it. There may be surprisingly little lime in chalk or lime-stone soil; it has leached, or percolated, down into the layers below. Iron in the soil may similarly leach down and form a layer of hard pan which hinders the spread of plant roots; if such soil is to be cultivated or afforested the hard pan must be broken up.

Soil and the Scenery

As every gardener knows, each soil favours the growth of some special plants; roses, for example, flourish on a clay soil. This applies to wild plants and trees as much as to garden flowers and, as the soil is formed by the rocks below, the different rocks each develop their own type of scenery.

South of London are two lines of hills only a few miles apart, one consisting of rolling grasslands with scattered woods, the other of heath and pinewood: the first is chalk country, with small patches of clay, the second is sandstone. Lime-stone produces bleak scenery, something like that of the chalk but wilder. Clay country is almost flat and very muddy in wet weather. Granite bosses form wild moorlands, of which Dartmoor is the best known. Basalt dykes and sills and lava-flows, being harder than the sedimentary rocks nearby, form great ridges, some of them miles long.

Great stretches of the same kind of rock cause many continental regions to be monotonously similar for wide areas, such as the steppes of Eurasia and the prairies and pampas of North and South America. The diversified scenery of Great Britain is largely due to the surprising variety of the rock-beds which underlie the compara-tively small island.

CHAPTER VIII

Underground Water and the Formation of Caves

SOME ROCKS, like clay, are impermeable or watertight; the rain either trickles downhill over them or collects on their surface. Others, like sandstone, are permeable or porous; the rain soaks into them and seeps downwards. Others, like granite, though themselves impermeable, have joints into which a little of the rain may penetrate.

The Water-table

Rain oozes downwards through porous rocks until it is checked by an impermeable layer below; here it accumulates so that, although the upper part of the rocks is almost dry, their depths are saturated with moisture. The surface of these saturated layers forms the water-table; it is neither horizontal nor parallel to the surface of the ground, but rises higher beneath the hills than below the valleys. Its level changes with the weather, rising during a rainy season and falling during the dry spells.

Springs and Wells

Wherever the water-table reaches the surface of the ground the water trickles out as a spring. If, during the summer, the table falls too low, the spring runs dry; but if, after heavy rain, it rises higher than usual, new springs appear and new streams form in valleys which are normally dry.

The water underground is tapped by pumps and wells. Holes are bored or dug downwards and, as soon as they reach below the water-table, they start to fill with water. This, of course, rises no higher than the table itself and shares its changes of level: during a drought the table may fall below the bottom of the well, which then runs dry—as it does if too many wells exhaust the underground water.

FIGURE 20. *The formation of a spring*

If the impervious bed slopes, the water seeps downwards over its surface, emerging as a spring where the junction of the beds outcrops. Here, where there is a natural water-supply, is a good site for a village. The line of villages between Epsom and Guildford in Surrey marks the junction of the chalk and the clay—and the pools beside the road near Epsom show how E-well got its name.

Where the porous beds forms a syncline between two impermeable beds, the water accumulates in its trough and may rise to touch the bed above. The water-table may, indeed, rise higher than the surface of the ground above it, being fed from hills some distance away; then a boring driven down to reach the porous bed will gush water like a natural fountain.

Such artesian wells are named after the Artois district, in France, where they have boiling. Calcite from the boiling water is deposited as a stony crust, forming the fur inside a kettle and threatening to choke boiler-pipes.

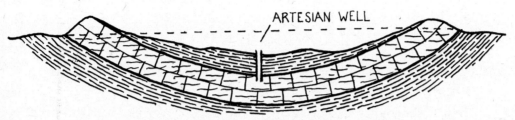

ARTESIAN WELL

FIGURE 21. *An artesian well*

long been used. The fountains in Trafalgar Square used to play naturally from artesian wells, but so much water has been drawn from the chalk below London that they have now to be driven by pumps.

Dissolved Minerals

The water of chalk or limestone country dissolves so much calcite that it gets hard; but this temporary hardness can be removed and the water softened, by

Similarly, hard water which evaporates in the open air deposits its calcite, so that the ground, and even the vegetation, is coated with a limy crust of calcareous tufa, also called travertine and sinter. There are regions in Italy where it accumulates at the rate of about three inches a month and is used as a building stone.

In the so-called petrifying springs in Derbyshire and in other limestone areas you can see an assortment of objects—

An artesian well—water spurting from a bore-hole in a Scottish quarry

One of the most famous of Britain's swallow-holes, Gaping Ghyll, Ingleborough, Yorkshire, is over 350 feet deep

kettles, jam-jars, and even nests full of eggs —being coated with calcite by the evaporation of the hard water from the limestone as it flows over them. You can leave something there and have it sent on to you when it has been "petrified" (an incorrect word, for it means "turned into stone", and these objects have only been coated with it).

Calcite is not the only substance which water dissolves from the rocks; other minerals also make the water hard, but they produce *permanent* hardness, which is not removed by boiling. Some make the water smell or taste, or even give it medicinal properties; a few mineral springs get such a reputation for healing that spas, like Harrogate in Yorkshire, Montecatini in Italy and Carlsbad in Bohemia, are

built round them. Chalybeate water contains so much dissolved iron that it not only tastes inky but leaves a yellow or reddish stain on the rocks.

Intermittent Streams

So much of the rain which falls on the calcareous rocks soaks into them that little is left to form streams and wear their surface away. That is why chalk, though not very hard, forms such lofty hills as the Chilterns and the Downs; limestone, which is harder, forms mountain ranges. These hills are trenched in many places by dry valleys, produced when the climate was wetter and the water-table higher.

In rainy weather some of these dry valleys may become bourns, intermittent streams and, during a drought, some of the ordinary streams may cease to flow and leave their valleys dry. The Mole in Surrey gets its name because during a hot summer its water is so much reduced that it all seeps into the ground, welling up again a little further downstream.

Caves

Water seeping down into the chalk may dissolve enough of it to form pipes, hollows a yard or so deep, but these soon fill in with material washed by the rain from the ground nearby. You can actually see these pipes only where the face of the chalk is exposed in a chalk-pit or cliff, but you may be able to detect their presence by a slight difference in the soil above them.

Limestone is so hard that it does not usually collapse even when rain and streams have pierced it with vertical swallow-holes (also called pot-holes) and tunnelled it with caves. Making its way along lines of weakness in the rock, the water may excavate a complicated series of tunnels ranging from great caverns to narrow crannies. It traverses the rock as an underground river whose course can be investigated by pouring dye into it as it flows into the ground and observing where the tinted water reappears.

These underground streams may change their course or run partly or wholly dry when the climate alters. Then the tunnels

An underground lake in the Mammoth Cave of Kentucky

they have excavated become caves, here broadening out into great echoing halls, there becoming mere fissures through which nobody can crawl. They may be completely dry, or streams may flow through them, widening in places to form subterranean lakes.

Some caves are very large indeed, the largest being in the United States: the

FIGURE 22. *The formation of caves in limestone*

61

Dripstone formation, called the Niagara Falls, *in the Carlsbad Caverns, New Mexico*

Mammoth Cave of Kentucky is many miles in length and consists of a complicated maze of tunnels linking underground caverns, some of them hundreds of feet high. These caves are inhabited by animals and their waters filled by fish (most of these animals are blind and some of the fish are colourless). In fact, it was the flight of an enormous number of bats, looking like a dark cloud of smoke, which led to the discovery of the Carlsbad Caverns of New Mexico.

A cavern may be so large that when the rocks above it are worn away by the weather, its roof falls in, converting it into a narrow canyon. This may be the origin of the Cheddar Gorge in Somerset, cutting through the Mendip Hills from north to south.

Dripstone: Stalactites and Stalagmites

Water flowing through the caves, like water on the surface, evaporates, and deposits some of its calcite. Trickling down over the cave walls, it coats them with a waxy-looking layer, or a lacy stone network, of dripstone. Flowing over the cave floor in a shallow stream, it forms a number of stony dikes.

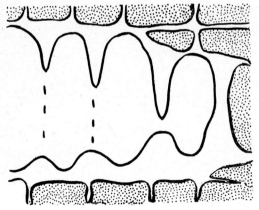

FIGURE 23. *Stalactites and stalagmites become rock pillars*

Water drips continually from many a cave roof and, before it falls, each drop evaporates slightly and leaves a speck of dripstone. Tiny as these specks are, they accumulate to form a stalactite, a calcite "icicle" suspended from the roof. Each drop, as it reaches the cave floor, similarly evaporates to leave another speck of dripstone. Here too, the specks accumulate to produce a stalagmite, a calcite mound. Growing towards one another, some of the two formations meet and blend into a dripstone pillar.

Cave Exploration

Cave exploration is a science, speleology, but it is also an interesting and exciting sport, "mountaineering in reverse". Like mountaineering, too, it can be very dangerous, so if ever you go caving you will have to take the greatest care. Go underground only with an experienced leader, and carry out his instructions implicitly. Your clothing should be warm, but so old that it will not matter when it gets dirty or torn. You will also need a good supply of food.

The special equipment will be arranged by your leader, but you yourself should carry some candles and matches (*not* "safeties") in a waterproof container, as well as spare batteries if you are using an electric torch, or reserve carbide (also in a waterproof container) if you are using acetylene flares. You will also want to have a personal first-aid kit.

Always be careful to keep with your party and resist any temptation to go off exploring on your own; to be lost underground, as I know from experience, is no joke, even if it ends happily; and some cave explorations have ended very unhappily indeed.

Abandoned mine-workings are even more dangerous to explore than natural caves, and you should leave them severely alone. There may be jagged ends of old truck-ways or lengths of wire to trap you, and you may come across the unguarded opening of a deep shaft. The roof may be supported with decaying pit-props ready to collapse at a touch. Such places should be investigated only by experts.

Geological students are sometimes allowed to descend mines which are still being worked—but only at their own risk. If you have an opportunity of visiting a mine, you must take care to follow any instructions you may be given and be careful not to obstruct the work. Such a visit is a privilege seldom granted to young students but they may be allowed to go over the works on the surface and to collect specimens from the refuse-heaps.

Stalactites and stalagmites in a Cheddar Gorge cave

CHAPTER IX

The Action of Rivers

YOU CAN see how a sudden cloud-burst, like the one which devastated Lynton, can turn a stream into a destructive torrent. You may find it harder to believe that the streams and rivers often destroy the land and have carved out the valleys through which they flow. As you watch the mountain rivulet murmuring pleasantly downhill, or the great river flowing peacefully over the plain, you may wonder how they could possibly do so much geological work.

If you see them during the winter you will understand. The rivulet has become a torrent and its murmur a roar. It scrapes the rock fragments it carries against its bed. The lowland river has become a swirling floor, irresistibly sweeping great tree-trunks along; its water is turbid with the silt it has ripped from the banks; and beside it are great stretches of water where it has overflowed.

The Slope of the River-bed

The further a river flows from its source the more gentle is the slope of its bed. At first the incline is quite steep, but further downstream it is more gradual; towards the river-mouth it hardly seems to slope at all.

The steeper the bed slopes, the faster the river flows. The head-waters flow so fast they wear the channel away; here the river's work takes the form of erosion. Towards its mouth the river travels so slowly that it lets fall some of the material it carries; here its work is deposition. For much of its course the river deposits about as much material as it wears away, its main task being transportation. Of course, its action varies with the season and the rainfall; a river in flood may erode its banks from its mouth right down to the sea.

River Erosion

River water dissolves more material from the rocks than does the rain. Not only does it contain carbon dioxide from the air, it absorbs other acids from the decaying vegetation on the moors, and these help to dissolve the limestone and chalk. When flowing over these rocks the water is surprisingly clear because of the dissolved calcite it contains.

The river also washes away the surface of loose-grained rocks, and carries off their fragments, along with the silt which the rain washes into it. The faster it flows, the greater is the material it can transport, and its power increases out of all proportion to its speed. If the rate of flow is doubled, the river's transporting power is increased not twice but sixty-fold; and if its speed is trebled, its power is increased several hundred times. A stream which usually transports nothing but silt may sweep great boulders along when it is in flood. By knocking and scraping the fragments together, it wears them smaller and blunts their edges: but, at the same time, the water "blankets" their impact so that grains of river-worn sand are not so smooth as the grains in a sand-dune.

D

A swift stream flows not smoothly but with a number of eddies like small whirlpools. These swirl the pebbles round, gradually grinding them away and at the same time boring circular or oval potholes (quite different from the large pot-

material from the land and sweeps it down to the sea; the quantity a really large river can carry is great indeed. The Mississippi, for example, transports about 400,000,000 tons of material every year, enough to lower its whole basin—the area

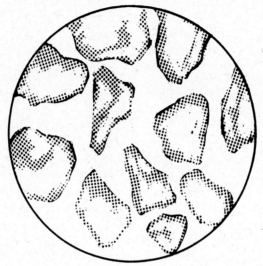

FIGURE 24. *River sand—the grains are comparatively angular and rough*

holes in limestone rocks) into the river-bed. During a drought you can see the pot-holes, not only beneath the water but in the dry part of its bed, where they were formed during the winter floods; lying in them may be the pebbles with which the stream bored them out.

A number of pot-holes may form side by side, separated only by thin walls of rock. These walls are at last worn away by the grit, or smashed away by the stones, which the river carries down-stream. So, even in the harder rocks, the river gradually deepens its bed. You can well imagine how much more quickly it acts when it scrapes jagged rock-fragments along a bed which is formed of sand, gravel or clay.

Transportation

Even the smallest stream wears some

which it drains—by one foot in three thousand years. If this rate of river erosion were the same everywhere, and if there were no earth movements to counteract it, then in something under 13,000,000 years all the land would be worn down to a flattish plain just above sea level.

Deposition of Silt

In the lower part of its course, where its flow is gentle, the river no longer wears away its bed. Instead, as the flow slackens, it begins to drop the material it carries: first the pebbles, then the larger sand-grains and, at last, even the finest silt. This produces a fertile soil, the alluvium, which derives its name from a Latin word meaning roughly the "downwash" of the stream.

During the winter the river overflows its banks, taking the alluvium with it;

Potholes in a river-bed—River Taff, Glamorganshire

The silting-up of a Scottish lake—Inchvallit, Inverness

River terraces and meanders in the valley of the Rio Grande, Texas

when the water subsides it drops this soil, leaving it spread over the ground. This is the origin of the alluvial plains which border the lower reaches of every large river and are likely to be flooded during the winter rains.

The retreating water drops more silt along the edge of its banks than elsewhere, forming ridges higher than the rest of the plain. In England, these are not large enough to be named. Those along the Mississippi, which are artificially streng-

thened to keep the river from flooding, are called levees, from the French *lever*, to raise.

When a river's flow is suddenly checked it deposits its alluvium almost at once. A swift-flowing tributary checked where it meets a slower mainstream forms an alluvial fan at a somewhat higher level than the river's flood-plain. A stream entering a lake may deposit so much alluvium as to form a small delta, which slowly extends down the lake, as has happened at Windermere and Derwent-water. Entering at the side of a long narrow lake, the stream's alluvium may cut the lake in two: Interlaken ("between the lakes") in Switzerland is built on the alluvium which separates the two lakes, Thun and Brienz. Thousands of years from now, some of the finest lakes in the English Lake District may be completely silted up, like some of the nearby stretches of flat country which used to be mountain tarns.

Deltas

Where a river enters the sea its flow may be not merely checked but actually reversed by the rising tide. Here a double load of silt is deposited, that brought down by the river and that swept into the river-mouth by the sea. The accumulated silt at last produces a whole tract of newly-formed land: in ancient times lower Egypt, from Cairo to the sea, used to be called "the gift of the Nile", because it plainly consists of silt brought down by that river's annual floods.

From that region we get the word delta, used for a tract of alluvium across which a river reaches the sea by several mouths. The Nile had two main channels; these, with the coast between their mouths, formed a triangle which reminded the Greeks of the letter delta Δ ("D") in their alphabet. Holland, much of which is so low-lying that it has to be protected by dykes, is the delta of the River Rhine.

The flow of a large river may be so strong that it continues even beyond the coast. Moving more slowly along the sides, where it is checked by the sea, the

River meanders in a flood-plain—West Dean, Cuckmere Haven, Sussex

current deposits its silt to form two parallel ridges, and flows along the channel between them. If it later changes its course, the current breaks through one of these ridges and forms two more going off at an angle; the channel it has abandoned soon silts up. The Mississippi, for example, flows for some distance into the Gulf of Mexico through several channels built by the alluvium it has brought down.

Why a River Meanders

A river flowing through soft rocks, like clay or sand or its own alluvial plain, wears away its banks rather than its floor. It seldom does so evenly; it usually attacks one bank more than the other. The smallest obstruction also deflects the flow, sending it obliquely against one bank and away from the other.

The river then erodes the bank towards which it is flowing. If the material which forms this bank is loose, it slides down into the water almost as fast as it is washed away. If the bank is more firmly built, the stream gradually undercuts its base, leaving the upper part to overhang—and give way suddenly if anyone treads on it. At last, the bank is so deeply undercut that its upper part falls away and collapses into the stream. For a time, the fallen material protects the newly-formed surface, but as soon as it is washed away the stream attacks the bank anew.

Meanwhile, on the other side of the stream, the flow slackens. Far from wearing this bank away, the water drops silt beside it. Enough of this silt may accumulate to form a spit of dry land projecting into the stream. At a sharp S-shaped bend two spits may form fairly close together, one projecting from each bank; this is a likely place to ford a river almost dry-foot. In the old days, when bridges were harder to build than they are now, a ford was a good site for a village

or town: that was how places like Oxford got their names.

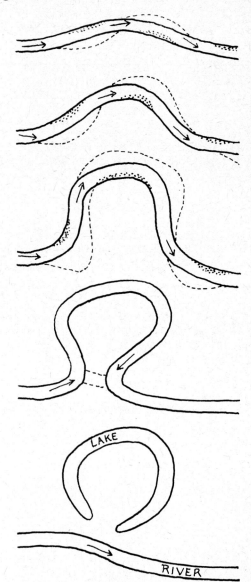

FIGURE 25. *The development of river meanders and ox-bow lakes*

The river may cut so deeply into one bank, and drop so much silt against the other, that it changes its course and forms a meander (the name comes from that of a very sinuous river in Asia Minor). The curve slowly increases and becomes a loop something like a horseshoe. Notice, for example, on the map, how the River Thames meanders round the Isle of Dogs, near Greenwich. In the warlike days of old a horseshoe curve was a natural moat protecting a fort or town within it: in this way Shrewsbury was defended by a meander of the River Severn.

For a time, the river flows down both channels but, at last, it forsakes its former

beside its course. When looking down on a valley from the hillside such abandoned meanders will show you where the river once flowed: a likely place for them is the edge of the valley where its floor meets its sides.

Incised Meanders

It sometimes happens that a river increases its strength or volume so much that it cuts right through the flood-plain

River terraces at Dalers, Nairn

course and travels round the loop. Later it attacks the narrow neck of land between the two ends of the loop and wears it completely away. But though it now leaves its meander, the new course the river cuts is unlikely to be exactly the same as its original one.

The ends of the meander soon get blocked with silt and it is converted into a long narrow curve of still water, an ox-bow lake. When the water evaporates the lake dries up; all that is left of what used to be part of a river is a curving dell

and down into the rocks below, deepening its bed while still keeping to its former meandering course. It then produces incised meanders: it winds as though it were crossing a plain, though it is now flowing through a narrow gorge, bordered by lofty cliffs.

There are splendid incised meanders in the lower Wye Valley. At Symond's Yat, where it crosses some softish sandstone, the River Wye forms a great loop across its flood-plain. Further downstream, where it traverses the harder limestone, the river has cut a deep gorge, overhung by steep, thickly-wooded slopes of cliffs. Even in these hard rocks the Wye has left two abandoned meanders, one of which, near

away the alluvium and to destroy its own valley-plain. Gradually, the river cuts down into its own bed, until it can go no deeper; then it starts to form a new

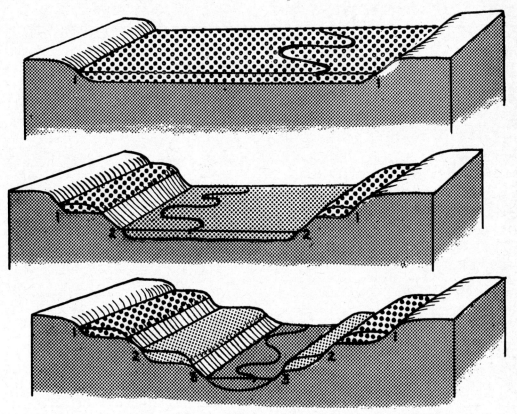

FIGURE 26. *A model showing the formation of river terraces.* (*Real terraces are never as regular or complete as this!*)

Newland, is several hundred feet above the stream. The Rheidol in Wales, the Wear between Durham and Sunderland, and the Moselle in Germany are rivers which have also cut incised meanders.

River Terraces

So long as a river keeps much the same size and speed, its alluvial plain stays at about the same level, no matter how often it is flooded, or what meanders it abandons and forms. But if the river gets larger or speeds up, if, as geologists say, it is rejuvenated, it at once begins to wash

valley-plain at a lower level. If it is rejuvenated once more it forms a third valley-plain still further below.

The river does not destroy the whole of its former plain, part of which remains as a capping to low flat-topped mounds rising from the valley-floor, part as ledges here and there on the valley sides. If the river has changed its level twice, there will be two sets of these river terraces at different levels. They consist of alluvium and other silty materials; buried in them may be found objects swept down by the river long ago: fragments of pottery, flint chippings, flint tools, shells, or animal bones.

The Thames, for example, has two river terraces, each named after one of the places where it was studied. The lower one, the Taplow Terrace, is about fifty feet above the river: Hyde Park, Holborn and the City of London are situated upon it to the north, and Putney to the south.

banks of some other river and intercept its waters.

The eroding action of a river not only widens or deepens its channel; it may also "cut back" its head, wearing away the ground from which it flows. In the mountains it scoops a valley-head out of the rocks. This is shaped something like half a funnel. Above it, the river wears

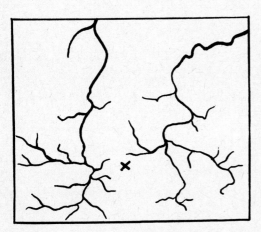 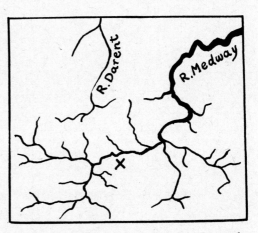

FIGURE 27. *River capture—how the Medway is thought to have captured the upper waters of the Darent, by cutting through the soft clay (marked with a cross)*

Its slope down to the present flood-plain, which is about twenty-five feet above water-level, can be seen at Exhibition Road, South Kensington.

The higher Boyn Hill Terrace, called after a place near Maidenhead, is about a hundred feet above the river. It forms several of London's commons, including Wandsworth, Clapham and Tooting. Pentonville, too, is situated on this terrace, and the slope down to the Taplow Terrace is traversed by the Pentonville Road.

River Capture

There are several ways in which a river can get larger or its flow become swifter. The climate may change and the rainfall increase. Earth movements may give the bed a steeper slope. Or it may breach the

the mountain ridge a little lower. This gives some mountain ranges their undulating sky-line, their crests being separated by saddle-shaped cols.

In the softer rocks of the lowlands, a river may cut back its head for some distance, along a bed of sand or clay or clean through a ridge. It may thus lengthen its channel so much that it cuts right into that of some other stream; being at a somewhat lower level than the stream it intercepts, it makes that stream's waters leave their original channel to flow into its own.

This river capture has two effects. It makes the river which did the capturing more powerful than before, so that it can cut back its head still further—perhaps into the channel of yet another stream.

The Iron Gates *on the Danube*

The stream whose water it captures is beheaded; in its lower reaches the flow is much smaller and more sluggish than before, and this makes the valley seem disproportionately large.

Several small streams used to flow more or less parallel northwards down the dip-slope of the Kent and Surrey hills into the Thames. But one of the tributaries of the Medway cut back its head westwards, along the clay bordering the foot of the hills, and captured the headwaters first of the Stour and then of the Darent. Further west, the Wey has similarly beheaded the Blackwater.

In the north of England four streams formerly ran from the Pennines and the Cheviots to the sea. The most powerful was the Tyne. One of its tributaries, the North Tyne, cut back its head and cap-

tured the headwaters of the Wansbeck and the Blyth; if it cuts back its head still further it may, in time, capture those of the Coquet.

River Gorges

When a river passes from soft to hard rocks its character changes. Instead of quietly traversing an open plain in sinuous curves its water now flows through a narrow gorge: it rushes impetuously forward with frequent eddies, made turbulent by the projecting rock-points and edges and by the inequalities of its floor.

Though one of Europe's greatest rivers, the Danube, flows peacefully for much of its course, wherever its valley narrows it swirls and rushes furiously along. At the Iron Gates, a gorge between the Carpathians and the Balkan mountains, it has a fall of about sixteen feet in two miles: a steamer can travel downstream through the Gates in about twenty minutes, but take two hours over the return journey. Though made navigable by a canal, the

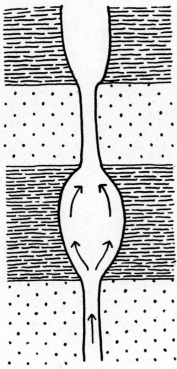

FIGURE 28. *The formation of river gorges—a river which cuts a wide channel in soft rocks can cut only a narrow gorge in hard rocks*

Gates are still a great menace to shipping.

The harder the rocks are, the deeper and narrower are the gorges and canyons which the river erodes. A British example is Lydford Gorge near Dartmoor. There are many fine gorges in the south of France. The finest, however, are in the United States, where broad, rapid rivers flow from regions of heavy rainfall over a plateau consisting of almost horizontal layers either of very hard rock or of alternate hard and soft rock.

In Arizona, a vast plateau extending from the base of the Rocky Mountains towards the Gulf of California is traversed by the powerful Colorado River. This originally eroded a broad valley about six miles wide and a thousand feet deep. Then the river was rejuvenated; something, perhaps an uplift of the rocks where it arose, speeded up its flow. At once it started excavating a deep channel downwards into its valley floor.

The surface of the plateau, formerly a shallow river valley, is now a desert, where there is no rain to wash away the edges of the channel and no vegetation to protect the rocks. Here the river and its tributaries cut their valleys ever deeper and deeper, so that they have produced a network of deep gorges, separated by great flat-topped buttresses, right through the sedimentary rocks and into the igneous rocks below. Hundreds of miles long and, in places, 6,000 feet deep though not a mile wide, and carved into vari-coloured rocks, the Grand Canyon of Colorado is one of the most magnificent sights in the world.

Waterfalls

When a river flows from hard rocks on to softer ones, it cuts a deeper channel below the junction than above. If the hard rocks dip gently downstream, the river passes calmly down their slope in a waterslide. If their face is jagged and irregular, it splashes over in a series of cascades. But if they dip upstream or are upright or horizontal, it plunges as a waterfall down into the deep channel which it has cut in the softer rocks below.

Just below the fall, the impact of the plunging water wears a deep basin or cauldron into the rocks, and its swirl wears them away, enlarging and deepening the cauldron. If the face of the waterfall consists of hard rocks overlying softer ones, the swirling water undercuts it and

Incised meanders—the River Wye near Chepstow

excavates a cave, which may be completely hidden behind the falling water.

As the hard rocks above are increasingly

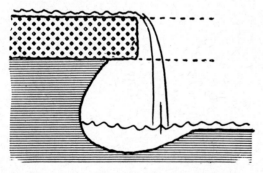

FIGURE 29.   *The formation of a waterfall*

undercut, their edge breaks away, so that the whole fall gradually works its way upstream.   In this way the river cuts a

deep gorge right through the rocks and, as it recedes, the gorge slowly lengthens.

When, in 1678, a French priest who had travelled into the unexplored region between the Great Lakes described the waterfalls he had discovered, they sounded too magnificent to be true.   Here the Niagara River crosses a great plateau where a bed of hard limestone, sixty to eighty feet thick, overlies a mass of soft shale and dips gently upstream.   Originally plunging in a great waterfall over the edge of the plateau, the river has gradually worked its way across it, cutting a deep gorge into the rocks.

The Niagara Falls—there are two, separated by Goat Island—have a drop of about 160 feet and a total width of about 3,000 feet.   The swirl of their waters has

The Iris Temple, *named after its multi-coloured rocks, in the Grand Canyon of Colorado*

The Victoria Falls on the Zambesi

The Niagara Falls

excavated a large cave, the Cave of the Winds, behind the falls and a gorge over 200 yards wide and 200 feet deep. They are slowly cutting back into the rocks at a rate of from four to five feet a day and, as the gorge is about seven miles long, they must have taken about 9,000 years to cut it.

Many waterfalls are formed where a sheet of lava, or a basalt sill, overlies the softer rocks. At the African Victoria Falls, discovered by Livingstone in 1855, the River Zambesi plunges over the edge of a thick layer of lava more than 1,800 feet wide, its drop ranging from 250 to nearly 400 feet. The falls are gradually working upstream along a joint plane in the lava and have produced a spectacular gorge.

CHAPTER X

The Action of the Sea

WHEN, ON a calm summer day, you are enjoying a seaside holiday, you may find it difficult to imagine how destructive the sea can be. A gale, even in summer, may change your opinion. But to get a real idea of the sea's power you should visit the shore during a stormy winter. Then you will see the breakers leaping over the esplanade or surging up the cliffs; you will feel the spray whipping your face; and you will hear the grinding roar of the pebbles as the waves rasp them over the rocks.

In the spring, you can see the effect of the winter gales. Raw-looking gashes on the cliff-face may show you where masses of rock have been torn away. Footpaths or roads may have had to be blocked because the sea has undermined them and brought part of them down. Cultivated fields may seem almost to overhang the sea where the cliff-edge is falling away. Buildings, once inhabited but now abandoned and derelict, may threaten to collapse into the sea.

Coastal Erosion

If ever a wave has knocked you off your feet you have a faint notion of the force with which great breakers pound the cliffs. They can deal several blows, of up to three tons to the square inch, every minute for days on end. Even if they consisted of nothing but water, the coastal erosion they produce would be very great.

But the waves do not consist only of water. They drive the air before them, and they hurl against the cliff and thrust across the beach large stones and masses of pebbles and sand. Even when receding they erode the shore with the pebbles and sand they drag seawards.

The waves not only drive air against the cliffs, they force it into all the cracks and crevices. Here it is strongly compressed and, as the waves retreat, it expands powerfully like the blast from a small bomb. Both when compressed and when expanding it widens the cracks and snaps off fragments of rock.

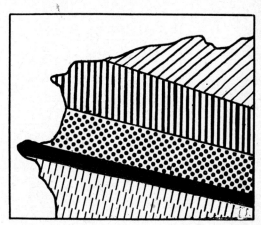

FIGURE 30. *Coastal scenery—a sketch map of part of the North Devon coast*

Like fresh water, brine expands when it freezes; then it too breaks fragments off the cliff-face; and, like the rain and the river, it dissolves the surface of such rocks as limestone and chalk. The cliffs, in the meantime, are eroded by the weather in the same way as the rocks on land.

Coastal erosion at Stead Hill, Kent

Formation of sea-stacks—Birchington Bay, Margate, Kent

F

A blow-hole—the outlet of a deep chasm worn in the rocks by the waves—High Stacks, Flamborough, Yorkshire

The waves act very unequally on different rocks. They rip away the soft rocks to form bays and inlets, leaving the harder ones to project as headlands and capes. Following lines of weakness along a joint or fault-plane, they excavate sea-caves and even cut through some narrow headlands to form natural arches like London Bridge near Torquay. By following lines of weakness behind a projecting rock, the waves separate it completely from the land, producing a stack, a small but lofty islet, like Old Harry near Swanage. By undermining the stack, they at last destroy it, as they have done to what was formerly Old Harry's Wife.

So the waves, aided of course by the rivers and the weather, by eroding at different rates the varied rocks which form Britain's shore, have given these islands their variegated coastline. They cut off from the land not only stacks which tower above the sea and islands large or small but

islets and reefs, some not visible except at high tide and others—a terrible menace to shipping—concealed by the water even at low tide.

Where the cliff-face consists of a vertical bed of hard rock, it acts like a wall protecting the softer beds behind. What happens when the sea breaches the wall? You can see this by visiting the so-called "Island" of Purbeck in Dorset. Here the strata run almost vertically; two outcrops of hard rock being separated by clay. At Swanage, the hard beds form two headlands, chalk on the north and limestone on the south, with a bay between them where the sea has eroded the clay. To the west, the two southernmost outcrops thin out, so that beyond Lulworth Cove the limestone is little more than a wall of rock protecting a narrow bed of clay.

At Stair Hole, the sea first breached a small tunnel in the limestone, and through this is scooped away the clay, forming a funnel-shaped gulf tapering down to the water's edge; then the rocks above the tunnel collapsed, cutting a gap in the limestone wall. At Lulworth itself there is a wider gap and the sea has eroded the clay to form the beautifully-circular Lulworth Cove. Still greater is the destruction at Worbarrow Bay. Further west, all that is left of the limestone is a line of reefs, the Cow and Calf, the Man o'War Rock and others, and a hammer-shaped headland pierced by an arch, the Durdle Door. Robbed of its protective wall, the clay has also been destroyed and the sea is now eroding the face of the chalk.

Further along the coast the destruction has been much greater. The limestone formerly extended westwards, but all that remains of it is the Portland peninsula. The chalk formerly extended eastwards: now all that is left of it is the Isle of Wight. Until the sea destroyed the intervening rocks, Portland, Purbeck and Wight formed part of a continuous outcrop; and a great river, a continuation of the Frome, fed by tributaries from the north and south, flowed eastward along a valley to its north. Part of this valley is now a strait, the Solent and Spithead.

Landslips

Much coastal erosion takes place gradually and, except for newly-formed scars on the cliff, there is little to show it occurred. But occasionally, especially where hard rocks rest upon a clay foundation, great masses of rock fall suddenly seawards and form a landslip at the foot of the cliff. In 1839, about thirty acres of cultivated land west of Lyme Regis collapsed unexpectedly, leaving a gap in the cliffs hundreds of yards long and forming a mass of tumbled material on the shore, the well-known landslip between Lyme and Axmouth. Other landslips produced the Warren near Folkestone and the Undercliff of the Isle of Wight.

Wave-cut Platforms

Part of the material fallen from the cliffs is soon carried away by the sea. Part is swept to and fro and ground together by the waves, and shifted back and fore by the tides. This sea-borne material acts much like the material transported by streams.

The jagged rock-fragments have their corners rubbed off and are smoothed to form pebbles. The waves grind them smaller and smaller and convert them into gravel and sand. They, meantime, rasp the surface of the intertidal rocks, breaking off their projecting edges and smoothing their surface. Eddies in the sea, like those in a river, whirl the pebbles about and bore pot-holes into the rocks.

Thus the sea produces a wave-cut platform, sloping gently from the foot of the cliffs into the sea. It is not smooth, for only part of its projections are worn away and holes are bored into it by some of the marine animals. But its general nature is easy to recognise in the striking difference between the wave-worn rocks of the platform and the jagged ones out of reach of the tide.

Along-shore Drift

The tides merely carry the fallen debris this way and that, but the current sweeps it along the coast; and, like a river, the faster it moves the heavier the material it can transport. When currents and tides work together, they produce a powerful flow which can transport heavy material; when they work against one another, the flow slackens and the heavier material is dropped. When the tide turns the debris is picked up again, to be dropped somewhat further on. In this way there is an intermittent along-shore drift of pebbles and sand up the Irish Sea and the English Channel and down the North Sea.

So powerful is this drift that it has to be checked artificially. Groynes, walls of timber or stone running down the beach into the sea, are built to intercept it. The way the sand and shingle pile up on the side facing the current shows how necessary these walls are. But for the groynes the drift would travel, unchecked, along the coast; in places it would obstruct the harbours, in others it would leave the coast open to destruction by the sea. The shingle and sand help to protect the coast from the waves' attack.

Along-shore drift is very powerful on the East Anglian seaboard, which consists of crag, low cliffs of clay and sand. Here, there has been much coastal erosion. England formerly extended further east than it now does; not only villages but whole towns have collapsed into the sea. The current takes so much loose material southwards that it has altered the

Rock arches, ancient and modern, at Bow Fiddle, Banff.   The cave in the foreground is a former rock arch on what is now a raised beach

Landslip—Totland Bay, Isle of Wight

course of the streams. The Alde no longer enters the sea near Aldeburgh: a lengthening bar of shingle has diverted its flow to the south so that it now runs parallel to the shore for about eleven miles. The Yare was similarly diverted southwards for about eight miles, but its bar so hindered navigation that it had to be cut through, giving the stream an artificial outlet about three miles south of Yarmouth. Swept southwards by the current, the severed portion of the bar helped to form Lowestoft Ness.

The Norfolk Broads are partly due to the southward drift of sand and shingle.

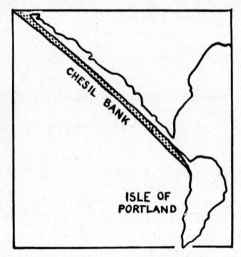

FIGURE 31. *Part of the Chesil Bank, Dorset*

Without this they would probably have been wide estuaries, but their mouths silted up and shut them off from the sea, converting them into large shallow lakes splendidly suited for yachting. The Broads, however, are largely artificial, having their origin in Medieval peat cuttings.

Formation of Beaches

Capes and islands check the movement of the sea and make it deposit the material it carries. In many of the bays and other

A sea-formed arch—Capri

inlets this produces a sea-beach of shingle or sand. As the water slows down, it roughly sorts the material, so that on parts of the beach the pebbles are larger, or the sand coarser, than elsewhere.

Chesil Beach, formed because Portland acts like a huge natural groyne, shows the result of the sea's sorting action. From near Portland, where the pebbles are up to three inches across, to the Beach's western end, near Abbotsbury (about eighteen miles away), they grade down to the size of peas.

A wind blowing at an angle shorewards sends the waves obliquely across the beach, carrying the pebbles and sand up it not perpendicularly but aslant. The waves retreat almost directly towards the sea and some of the material goes with them,

85

Moving sand-dunes.   Sea-sand, driven inland by the wind, is burying a forest at Maviston, Scotland, but is being "bound" by the planting of grass

travelling not straight up and down the beach but along it in a series of lop-sided "V"s.   This motion helps to pile the material up against the groynes, and the groynes keep it from being swept far along the coast.

The Growth of the Land

The sand on an open beach is too unstable to remain permanently; the waves swirl it along and the wind blows it away. Only when it is bound by such hardy plants as marram grass can other plants grow upon it and transform it into soil. Thus it is converted into part of the land.

If you look eastwards from the Kent coast near Reculvers, the hills which loom over a broad stretch of lowland may remind you of an island seen across the sea.   This will make you realise how the "Isle" of Thanet got its name.   Within

historical times it was a real island, separated from the Kentish mainland by a channel broad enough to shelter shipping.   Having been silted up, the channel

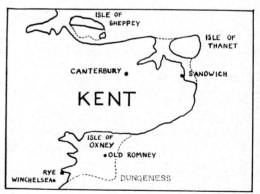

FIGURE 32.   *Changes in the coastline of Kent*

is now a stretch of fertile meadowland.
Much of the low-lying country on the south coast of Kent was also formed in

fairly recent times; Pevensey Level and Romney Marsh were once parts of a bay between Hythe and Winchelsea. The ancient Cinque Ports used all to be on the coast: notice on a large-scale map where four of them are now: Sandwich, Romney, Winchelsea and Rye.

The Beginning of Britain

If you look at old maps, which are valued as curios, and compare the coastline as they show it with its present appearance, you may get a surprise. In some places, new stretches of flat country have formed along the shore. In others, much of the land has been worn away. Much more would have been destroyed, too, were it not for artificial sea-defences constructed along the coast.

Still greater was the destruction which even the oldest map will fail to show you, for it occurred before the earliest maps were drawn. Two famous French geologists were among the first to realise this.

When Guettard was mapping the rocks of north-west France he noticed how the English Channel seemed to cut them short. They must, he inferred, continue on the opposite coast—and a book on the "natural rarities" of Britain confirmed that he was right.

Later, French thinkers offered a prize for the best essay on the problem of whether England had ever been united to France. It was awarded to Desmarest because his essay, instead of being merely theoretical, was based on his own studies of the rocks on both sides of the Channel.

Not only do similar rocks face one another across the Channel, they show that they have been affected by the same earth movements. The axis of the Wealden anticline extends into France a little south of Calais, and that of the Isle of Wight anticline not far from Dieppe.

Long ago—though quite recently by geological standards—Britain actually formed part of the Continent, and the Thames was a tributary of a gigantic river, a continuation of the Rhine, which flowed northwards across a land which extended northwards beyond what is now the Dogger Bank. During the Great Ice Age, the flow of the water was diverted by the ice-sheet which blocked the North Sea. Turning south, its newly-formed Channel severed the British Isles from the mainland. This process was helped, too, by rock-boring marine animals whose tunnels so weakened the rocks that they were easily worn away.

The face of a glacier—the Columbia Glacier, Alaska (its height may be judged from the size of the men in the boat)

Roches moutonées in Owen's Valley, California. The slanting rays of sunshine make these glacier-polished boulders look like a herd of sheep

CHAPTER XI

The Action of Moving Ice

IN 1826, a Swiss naturalist, Louis Agassiz, studied the Alpine valleys, investigating a theory that the glaciers had formerly extended further down them than they did in his own time. He soon found that this was true. Then his work in other countries led him to put forward a theory so surprising that other geologists were slow to accept it; that vast regions, now temperate, had once been covered with ice.

Rivers of Ice

Near the Poles, and on lofty mountain-tops, the weather never gets warm enough to melt the snow. Instead, this accumulates in immense snowdrifts, some of which melt and freeze again to form icefields. During the spring thaws, quantities of the snow and ice begin to melt and collapse down the mountain-sides, taking much surface material with them, as avalanches. But vast masses, the glaciers, travel down the slopes and along the valleys like slow-moving rivers of ice.

Though ice cannot flow freely, like water, it melts slightly when strongly compressed and freezes again in a slightly

Glacial striae, in the Rosyth Dock-yard, Fife

different position. This enables the glacier to fit itself into the shape of the valley, to turn corners and to surmount obstacles in the valley-floor. Slowly though it moves, perhaps only a few inches a day, its great weight gives it tremendous thrusting-power.

Fragments from the slopes above the glacier, loosened by the weather, drop on to the edges of the glacier in two long lines of scree, forming lateral (side) moraines. When two glaciers meet where their valleys converge, they move forward together and their inner lines of scree combine to produce a medial (central) moraine. Where a large glacier has been formed by the merging of several smaller ones, its surface is strewn with loose morainic material, ranging from masses of earth to jagged lumps of rock. Some of this material falls into the crevasses which open, here and there, in the ice. The glacier then drags it along over the valley-floor and against its sides.

The powerful thrust of the moving ice also scrapes more material from the valley floor and sides and grinds it against the rocks. This both rubs their surface smooth and scores it with fine parallel lines (glacial striae) and crushes much of the loosened material into a very fine dust, rock flour.

In Alaska, many large glaciers extend beyond the mountain valleys into the plains, covering vast areas with immense ice-fields. Over much of Greenland, and almost the whole of Antarctica, the ice-

The junction of two glaciers—the Theodul and Gorner Glaciers, near Zermatt, Switzerland

fields cover even the high ground, only the mountain summits projecting as the jagged nunataks.

When glaciers reach the sea they "calve" into icebergs, which drift away with the current; they then drop morainic material on to the sea-floor, producing such shallows as those off Newfoundland. On land, when they pass below the snow-line, they melt to form rivers whose water is turbid with rock flour. The rock fragments they carry pile up as a terminal moraine, a ridge of morainic material crossing a valley and sometimes forming a natural dam. But, in regions whose climate gets gradually milder, so that year after year the glacier melts a little higher up its valley, it strews the material more evenly over the valley floor.

Traces of Bygone Glaciers

When a glacier retreats it leaves unmistakable signs of its former presence. The depths of the valley where it used to flow, smoothed by the moving ice, look very different from the rugged weather-worn rocks above. The valley floor is littered with morainic material, some of it piled up as the one-time terminal moraines. The rocks, though smooth, are scored with glacial striae. The great boulders, too, massive for even the moving ice to dislodge, are, except on their downstream side, smooth, rounded and striated. The ends of the spurs which project into the valley have been ripped away by the tremendous thrust of the moving ice.

These signs of glaciation are visible not only in Alpine and other mountain valleys but even in many lowland regions. They enable us to distinguish which regions were once covered with ice. There is a striking difference between the rocks over which the glaciers have travelled and those which were out of their reach. The former are smoothed and striated; some bear two sets of striations crossing one another, showing that the ice travelled in different directions at different times.

Projecting above the bracken you may see rocks which look something like the backs of sheep—hence their name, *roches moutonnées*, which comes from the French. They are smoothed and rounded; if one side, or one end, is rough, it shows you, like the striations, the direction in which the glacier travelled, for it faces away from the moving ice.

Valleys Smoothed by Glaciers

The cross-section of a valley eroded by a stream looks something like the letter "V", its sides sloping right down to the flood plain, and their spurs projecting far across it. The cross-section of a glaciated valley is more like the letter "U", for the thrust of the ice has worn its sides into a curve and nipped off the ends of the spurs.

In such a valley, too, the ice has scooped away the slopes down which the tributaries flowed, so that they now reach the main stream from hanging valleys high above its floor. So steep are some of the valley sides that the tributaries plunge over them as waterfalls; most of the falls in the Lake District, like those in the Alps, are over the ends of the hanging valleys.

In the mountain slope from which the glacier arises, the rocks, instead of sloping straight down, have a U-shaped curve, so that they look not like a funnel but like a basin. There is no English name for these basins; in Scotland they are called corries and, in Wales, cwms; most geologists use the French word, *cirques*. Some of them contain tiny lakes, naturally dammed by the last terminal moraine which the glacier produced before it melted away.

Further down the valley there may be larger lakes, dammed by earlier terminal moraines. Though these mostly consist of loose rubble, there is enough clay in

V-shaped and U-shaped valleys
1. *Near Trevique Farm, Cornwall*
2. *Near Newadd Reservoir, Brecon*

them to make them watertight. Many lakes in Scotland and Wales, as well as in the Lake District, are penned in by morainic dams.

The glacier itself may dam the water in a side valley to form a lake. In the Alps, the Aletsch Glacier has formed the Marjelen Sea. In Alaska, the Muir Glacier has formed Berg Lake, which is

its course. Its head-waters still flow northwards, as of old, towards the Irish Sea, but ice on the Cheshire plain dammed them to produce the bygone Lake of Lapworth—named after the geologist who first realised it had once existed. The spillway that its waters found was on the east, near Ironbridge. Here, they cut a gorge so deep that the Severn still flows

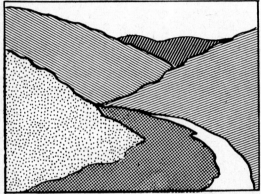 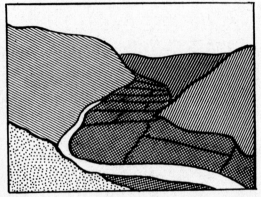

FIGURE 33. *V-shaped and U-shaped valleys. The unglaciated valleys of Devon contrasted with the valleys in North Wales*

four miles long, and Main Lake, which is seven miles long.

Penned in and rising behind the glacier, the waters of such a lake may overflow and find a spillway through some depression in its bank. In their flow they may cut the spillway so deep that they go on using it, instead of their former outlet, which was dammed by the moraine even after the glacier melted. By this process, a river may completely change its course.

The Derwent, which rises not far from the Yorkshire coast, seems to have originally flowed almost direct to the sea. But, when it was dammed by the ice, its waters rose, forming a broad lake covering the Vale of Pickering. The lake found a new spillway to the west and so the Derwent now flows away from the sea and on, by way of the Ouse, into the Humber.

The Severn also seems to have changed

through it reaching the sea through the Bristol Channel.

Along the sides of a valley near Ben Nevis there are three horizontal ledges. Geologists long wondered how they were formed and, at first, thought that, like the raised beaches along the shore, the ledges show former differences in the sea-level. These parallel Roads of Glenroy are now believed to consist of beach deposits formed not by the sea but by the lake produced in the Glen when its streams were dammed by glaciers; like the river terraces in the Thames Valley, they mark the different levels which the water formerly reached.

Unlike water, moving ice can scoop out depressions in the surface over which it flows; when the ice melts they become mountain tarns and lakes. Some of these rock basins are high up in the mountains,

A hanging valley—Cautley Spout, Westmorland. This stream formerly ran down the gulley at the right of the illustration

like Glaslyn in North Wales; but they may even be below sea level, like Loch Coruisk in the Isle of Skye.

The Glacial Drift

The glaciers not only dammed lakes in mountain valleys, ripped away the projecting spurs of the hills and smoothed and scored the rocks. They also transported much morainic material far across the land, leaving it strewn about the ground when the ice melted. This material includes great boulders, the erratics, which have been brought from long distances; pieces of rock in South Wales have been identified as detached fragments of Ailsa Craig, in the Firth of Clyde.

These erratics may be found in the most unlikely places, balanced rather precariously high up on the valley sides: for example, in Llanberis Pass. There is only one way of accounting for the position of these perched blocks: that they were carried from the glaciers and left

Lake dammed by a terminal moraine—Llyn Caer, Pen-y-Cader, Wales

where they are by the melting ice.

Most of the material the glaciers transported consisted of a medley of smaller boulders, jagged fragments of stone, and rock flour now converted into clay. Gravels swept along by the torrents flowing from the melting ice show the usual signs of deposition by water; some are stratified and are roughly sorted in order of size.

Boulder clay (also called, because of its origin, glacial clay) is neither sorted nor stratified; it consists of pieces of rock of all sizes embedded in the fine clay formed from rock flour. Some of the fragments, though not rounded like pebbles nor jagged like a scree, are smoothed and striated like perched blocks.

In the hills, boulder clay spreads over the floor of the valleys. In the lowlands, it forms a thick layer covering much of the ground, and rivers carve their channels through it in the usual way. It may be a mere surface coating, with gaps here and

Perched block—Cunyon Crags, Northumberland

The parallel Roads of Glen Roy

there, but at its thickest it forms lofty cliffs and even extends beyond the older rocks to form stretches of land.

All this ice-transported material, gravels and boulder clay, form the glacial drift. North of the River Thames, there is so much of this material that two separate series of geological maps are needed. The Drift Edition includes the glacial material and shows the rock-beds below only where they appear through its gaps; these maps are used wherever knowledge of the subsoil is required, as in agriculture, forestry and land utilisation.

The Solid Edition ignores the glacial deposits and shows the outcrops of the underlying rocks just as if the drift were not there at all. These maps are necessary in industries such as mining; and, for general geological work, they show the structure of the land much more clearly than the Drift Edition.

The Great Ice Age

Study of the glacial drift shows that during the Great Ice Age, which lasted hundreds of thousands of years and ended about twenty thousand years ago, the Arctic ice-cap extended far to the south. Britain was ice-bound as far as the Thames, as were much of northern Eurasia and the area of North America north of the Great Lakes. Even south of the ice-cap conditions were very bleak; the mountains were largely covered by glaciers and much of the lowlands buried by the snow.

Layers of sand and gravel interbedded with the drift show that there were three interglacial periods during which the climate grew milder and some of the ice thawed. Then conditions hardened again and the land was ice-bound anew.

Traces left by the glaciers indicate the direction in which they moved. Much of the ice which covered Britain came from Scandinavia, though some spread outwards from the snow-capped mountains of Scotland, Northern Ireland and Wales.

This was not the only ice age the world has experienced, but it is the one whose effects are mostly clearly shown on the scenery. The Chilterns, for example, are more densely-wooded than the Downs, which were beyond the ice-cap, though both are formed of chalk. In the mountains which once were glaciated, the valleys have been widened and straightened and given a "U" instead of a "V" section and blocks are perched on their slopes. Some of the boulder clay which extends so widely over the land is rather featureless; elsewhere, it forms an undulating countryside of alternate ridges and depressions, including a number of drumlins, oval "whale-back" mounds. Some of the terminal moraines left as the ice retreated form prominent ridges; one extends about three thousand miles inland from the Massachusetts coast.

CHAPTER XII

Minerals

THERE ARE hundreds of different minerals and they are fascinating to collect. But although they form every rock there is, you may be surprised how difficult they are to find. Much depends on where you look for them. There are very few in sedimentary beds; the best come from igneous rocks. Specimens in the local museum will help you to identify their fracture and cleavage, the way they break and split; and by their hardness and weight. A few are magnetic, or have a distinctive lustre (gleam), or feel—or even taste. The type of rock you find them in is a help: in limestone, a six-sided transparent crystal is likely to be calcite; in granite, it would be quartz.

Many minerals form crystals with flat

FIGURE 34. *An ore-bearing vein lined with crystals of another mineral*

them, and will show you which of them you are likely to find in the regions nearby.

Identifying Minerals

Skill in identifying the minerals comes with practice. You are helped by their colour and transparency, though they may be discoloured by impurities; by their streak—the mark they leave on paper; by the shape of the crystals they form; by faces and straight edges and there are several crystal forms. When studying a crystal you should notice whether it has four or six main faces, and whether the faces are at right-angles or askew. A crystal with square faces is a cube; one with oblong faces, a prism; one with triangular faces meeting in a point, a pyramid; prisms ending in a pyramid are fairly common. Some crystals are twinned; they look as if they had been split in half and then reunited with one half turned right round.

Ores and Mineral Veins

Sulphur and a few metals, like gold and silver, occur "native" (pure) but most metals have to be smelted from their ores. These are easy to distinguish from the

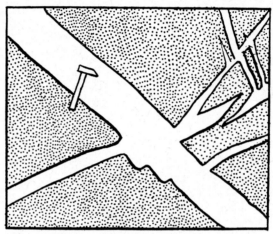

FIGURE 35. *Mineral veins may intersect in complicated patterns. This sketch shows light-coloured veins in granite. The hammer (shaft about a foot long) gives the scale*

other minerals, for they are heavier and have a metallic look. Many form lodes (veins) in the rocks.

The Ores of Iron

The principal ore of iron is haematite (iron oxide). It may form crystals but it is found chiefly in great black or dark grey masses; its streak is red and it looks bright red if you scratch or powder it. Its broken surface has a fibrous structure, but its unbroken outer surface looks so nubbly that haematite is sometimes called "kidney iron ore".

Limonite (an iron oxide which is hydrated—it contains water) is yellow or brown and gives a brownish streak. Bog iron ore, formed by decaying plants, which gives the water of moorland swamp

its brown colour, is a form of limonite.

Magnetite (another oxide of iron) is easy to recognise by its effects on the compass needle; you can pick up its powder with a magnet. It is iron-black and forms very few crystals. In Siberia, and some other countries, it is an important ore of iron.

Inexperienced prospectors out gold-hunting have often been deceived by a gleaming yellow metallic-looking substance; hence the impolite name of "fool's gold" for iron pyrites (iron sulphide). The mistake is easy to understand: this ore, with its brassy appearance and metallic lustre, really looks like gold, though its streak is brownish-black. It occurs in veins or nodules and forms cubic or twelve-sided crystals whose faces are striated (marked with fine parallel lines); it forms flecks on coal, and fossils coated with iron pyrites look very attractive.

Marcasite, which occurs as brown nodules in chalk, is another form of iron sulphide. It is a gleaming silver mineral, looking like "needles" radiating from a centre; the brownness of its outer surface is due to rust.

Clay ironstone is more of a rock than a mineral: it consists of clay, saturated with siderite (iron carbonate). It forms the iron pan in the sandstones south of London where it was once an important ore—some of the hillocks in the Vale of Holmesdale are old slag-heaps covered with vegetation. It is no longer worked, however, for other iron ores are so much richer.

The Ores of Copper

You can recognise the ores of copper by their bright colour. This, and its greater softness, distinguishes copper pyrites (chalcopyrites, copper and iron sulphide) from iron pyrites. When iridescent, gleaming with several bright colours, it is called "peacock copper ore".

Two copper carbonates are so brightly-coloured that they are used for ornamental work. Chessylite is also called azurite because of its brilliant blue colour; its crystals have a needle-like structure. Malachite is bright green and forms rounded masses; if you break these open you will see that their broken surface is alternately light and dark green. Ruby copper (cuprite, copper oxide) is bright red and forms ten-sided or twelve-sided crystals.

The Ores of Lead, Zinc and Tin

As you would expect, galena (lead sulphide), the principal ore of lead, has a grey, "leaden" look and is quite soft and very heavy. It forms cubic crystals which you can easily crumble down into tiny cubes.

You might easily confuse zincblende (sphalerite, zinc sulphide) with galena, for it too is soft and forms cubic crystals. The blende is, however, much lighter and its crystals have a conchoidal (oyster-shell) fracture. It usually has a metallic lustre, and it may be yellow, brown, or very dark—hence its name, "black Jack".

Tinstone (cassiterite, tin oxide) resembles galena in its heavy weight, but it is harder and its colours range from white or grey to dark brown; its crystals have a brilliant lustre. As stream tin it forms nodules in river beds and gravels near its lodes.

The Ore of Uranium

In 1896, the French physicist Antoine Becquerel found that some photographic plates had mysteriously become fogged; then he realised that he had left them near a compound of uranium. This accidental discovery of radio-activity finally led to the construction of the atomic and hydrogen bombs, and to the peaceful use of atomic energy.

The principal ore of uranium is its oxide, pitchblende. This gets its name from its "pitch black" look; it is rather hard and it is heavier even than lead. It is radio-active and will fog any undeveloped photographic plates or films or paper that are left near it.

Quartz

The commonest non-metallic mineral is silica (silicon dioxide). As quartz it helps to form granite and other igneous rocks. Its grains, coloured by iron, form much of the sandstone. Its crystals are six-sided, many of them being prisms ending in a pyramid; some are marked with striations; they are too hard to scratch with a knife.

Transparent and colourless in its pure form as rock crystal, quartz tinted with impurities forms other ornamental stones. Amethyst is violet; smoky quartz (cairngorm) is brown; rose quartz is pink; milky quartz is white. Jasper is red, and opal changes colour according to the direction of the light. Chalcedony, the purple, grey, or brown lining to some hollow flints, is another form of quartz; agate is chalcedony in layers of different colours.

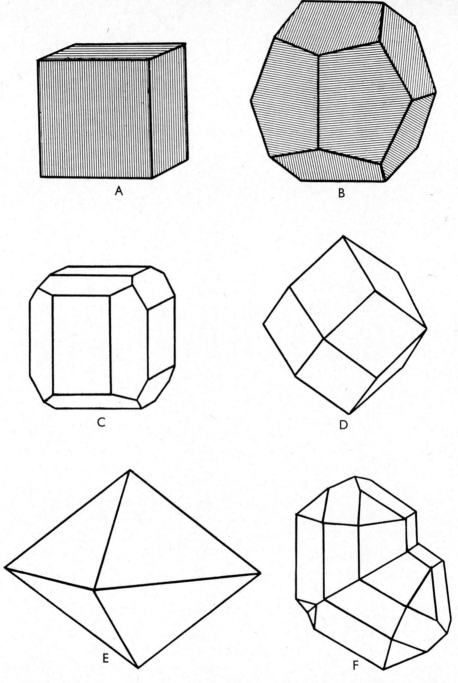

FIGURE 36

A. *Iron pyrites—striated cube*
C. *Iron pyrites—combination of cube and pyritohedron*
E. *Tinstone*

B. *Iron pyrites—twelve-sided pyritohedron*
D. *Magnetite*
F. *Tinstone (twinned)*

Flint consists of silica blackened by organic material; broken and smoothed by the waves, it forms the pebbles found in so many pudding-stones. Of all the earth's minerals, flint has been the most useful to man, for it provided him with tools and hunting-weapons long before the first metal was ever smelted.

Calcite

Calcite, which forms the greater part of chalk and limestone, is colourless or white when pure, but much of it is tinted by iron or other minerals. Its crystals are six-sided, like those of quartz, but they are easily distinguished, for they are not striated and can be scratched with a knife; in "nail-head spar" its pyramids are almost flat, in "dog-tooth spar" they are long and sharply pointed. It consists of calcium carbonate and will fizz if you touch it with a drop of weak acid.

Iceland spar is a very pure form of calcite; it is quite transparent but, by splitting the beams of light which pass through it, it makes everything you see through it look double. This makes it very useful in industry and in geology; with a polarising microscope, in which two thin plates of Iceland spar are used, you can identify the different minerals in a slice of rock ground thin enough to be transparent.

Pearl spar (dolomite) is a carbonate of calcium and magnesium and forms dolomitic (magnesian) limestone. It resembles calcite, but is harder. Its crystal faces are very slightly curved, and it may be pale brown or yellow with a pearly lustre.

Rock-salt and Fluor-spar

The taste of rock-salt (halite, sodium chloride) is unmistakable. White or colourless when pure, this mineral is

Vein of pyrites in shale—Parys Mountain, Anglesey

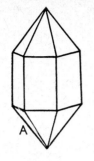

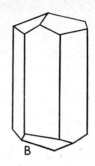

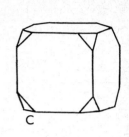

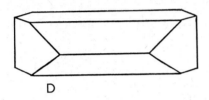

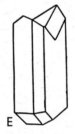

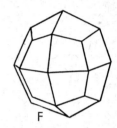

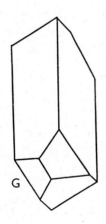

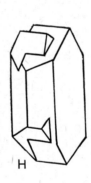

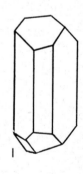

FIGURE 37

A. *Quartz*
D. *Barytes*
G. *Orthoclase felspar*

B. *Calcite*
E. *Selenite*
H. *Plagioclase felspar (twinned)*

C. *Fluor-spar (cleaved across corners)*
F. *Garnet*
I. *Plagioclase felspar*

commonly stained red or yellow with iron. It is very light and very soft and dissolves easily in water—in fact, it is hygroscopic (attracting moisture from the air) and unless you keep it tightly corked up it will dissolve itself into a pool of brine. Its crystals are small cubes, with hollow faces, and its cleavage is parallel to its faces.

Fluor-spar (calcium fluoride) also crystallises in cubes, but it cleaves, rather surprisingly, not parallel to their faces but across them; if you gently tap the corner of a fluor-spar cube it will fall off, leaving a new triangular face askew to the others. Though rather light and soft, it is somewhat harder and heavier than rock-salt. It may be glassy-looking, white, green, yellow, purple or blue; "Blue John", a very beautiful form of fluor-spar found in Derbyshire, is much used for ornamental work.

Gypsum and Barytes

Gypsum (hydrated calcium sulphate) is another soft light mineral, white or iron-stained pink; in the Midlands of England it forms masses several feet thick. It also forms large crystals, many of which are twinned, in some of the sandy beds; because of their lustre, these are called selenite, from the Greek for moonstone, although they do not contain the element selenium; those with a fibrous, silky look are also called satin spar.

Barytes (barium sulphate) is easy to recognise because, although it is not a metallic ore, it is surprisingly heavy; its name comes from the Greek for weight, and it is sometimes called heavy spar. When pure, it is transparent or translucent, but it is usually stained yellow or pink, and it has a glassy lustre; it crystallises in flat tablets.

The Silicates

Pure quartz consists of silica, but silica is not only a mineral. It is also the basis of silicic acid, which combines with some metals to form a very large number of other minerals, the silicates.

There are many types of felspar, the mineral which gives granite its red or white colour, and they are classified in two main types. Orthoclase (splitting straight) felspar, which cleaves at right angles, is a silicate of potassium and aluminium; some of its crystals are twinned. The many plagioclase (splitting askew) felspars, which cleave obliquely, are silicates of sodium, calcium and aluminium; many of their crystal faces, though not actually striated, are marked by faint parallel lines: this is a special form of twinning.

Mica forms the tiny black gleaming specks you see in granite; you may even notice them in paving-stones. It also produces large crystals; they consist of very thin layers which you can easily split off, transparent and slightly flexible and elastic. Like felspar, it includes several different types: white mica (Muscovite—much of it comes from Russia) is a hydrated potassium and aluminium silicate; black mica (biotite) also includes magnesium and iron.

Two other silicates are fairly common. Garnets (silicates of several metals) are the small reddish or brown crystals formed in some of the metamorphic rocks; the more ornamental ones, especially the blood-red carbuncle, are semi-precious stones. Serpentine (hydrated magnesium silicate) is both a mineral and a rock; it has an attractive mottled appearance and, at the Lizard in Cornwall where it forms a large outcrop, is much worked into ornamental souvenirs.

There are so very many silicates, and the element silicon in some ways so much resembles carbon, that the suggestion has been made that under conditions of intense heat and pressure, such as must have prevailed in the world's early days, it might produce living creatures. If so, the silicates may be the "fossils" of stone "plants" and "animals" which inhabited the earth before it was cool enough to make life based on protoplasm—a compound of carbon—possible! Exciting as this idea seems, however, geologists do not take it very seriously.

CHAPTER XIII

Fossils

Buried in the rocks are objects which look like stone animals and plants. These "figured stones", as they used to be called, greatly puzzled the early naturalists, who tried hard to explain them. These objects, they said, were simply freaks of nature, ordinary stones which just happen to have a queer shape; they were sea-creatures which had somehow got formed on land instead of in the water and so were made of stone instead of flesh and blood; they were a sort of trial run by nature before it got down to the mass-production of animals and plants; or they were stones moulded into shape by "plastic forces" in the rocks—or maybe by the influence of the stars!

Leonardo da Vinci was one of the thinkers who realised that the figured stones are really what they look like, the remains of living creatures buried in the silt. But, whereas many other thinkers thought that they had been buried during Noah's Flood, he saw that this was impossible.

The Science of Ancient Life

In the seventeenth century, the English scientist Robert Hooke explained that the Flood could not possibly have lasted long enough to account for so very many stones. As some of them resemble the shells of tropical animals, he pointed out, they show that the climate of southern England, where they were found, must once have been far warmer than it is now. As for their being freaks of nature, he said

sarcastically that nature was far too serious to make practical jokes.

Hooke realised, too, that the figured stones are not mere curios, interesting or amusing to collect. Thinkers, he complained, were far too heedless of "such a trivial thing as a rotten shell", for it could

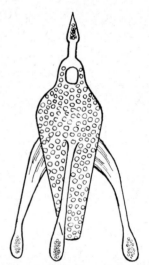

FIGURE 38. *A modern invertebrate—radiolarian*

be a far better clue to the earth's history than an ancient coin. Difficult though it was to understand the stones, he foresaw that this would one day be possible.

The more the figured stones were studied, the clearer became their nature. At last they came to be known as fossils, from a Latin word which means dug up. This, at first, meant anything unusual found in the earth, but it is now used to describe vestiges of the living creatures of old—though we do also speak of "fossil" rain-prints and ripple-marks. Another new word was coined for their study: palaeontology, from the Greek for "the science of ancient life".

How Fossils have been Preserved

Not all fossils consist of the actual remains of living creatures; some are simply the impressions they left in the rocks. A sea-shell, for example, gets covered with silt, which hardens into stone, fitting completely around it. When the shell decays it leaves a mould, a hollow in the rock showing an exact impression of its surface. When an animal has died and the silt seeps in to fill its shell, and hardens inside it, this forms an interior mould, an impression of the shell's inner surface.

When interior and exterior moulds have solidified, and the shell which formed them has decayed, more of the silt may seep in to take its place. When this hardens it reproduces the surface of the shell in faithful detail. This is a cast. Both words, mould and cast, come from terms used in metal-working and sculpture.

The moulds and casts were never part of the living creature; they are simply impressions of its shape in the rock. If you break them, you will find that they are just pieces of stone differing very little from the rocks around them. It is only on the surface that they resemble animals or plants.

Yet, superficial though it is, this resemblance is exact so far as it goes, and it tells us much about the creatures themselves. It even gives us an idea of their bodies, although even before they perished these were too soft to leave any trace on the rocks. On the interior casts or moulds of a sea-shell you may find markings showing how the animal's muscles were attached. Equally well, study of modern creatures of similar type will give

you an idea of the build and action of those muscles.

Other fossils are much more than an impression in the rocks; they are the remains of plants and animals which have become petrified (turned into stone). So completely has calcite or silica or iron pyrites soaked into them that it has replaced every particle of their bodies. This produces fossils which, though made of stone, resemble the original creatures not only on the surface but in every detail. They are easier to study than the creatures themselves, for they never decay; they are hard and firm instead of soft and flabby; and they can be cut into thin slices and then ground down until they are transparent enough to be mounted on glass slips for examination under a microscope.

Other fossils consist not of stone but of those parts of an animal or plant which are too hard to decay, being formed of calcite or silica or a horny substance, chitin. The parts most likely to be preserved are shells, teeth, bones and tree-trunks and roots. There are fossils, too, which merely form a thin coating on the surface of a rock or a shell. Examples are the stems and leaves of the trees which produced coal; graptolites which look rather like pencil-marks on the rocks; and sea-mats which look rather like lace.

Some animals have been killed in surroundings which preserved their whole bodies. Amber, for example, is a fossil gum, which entrapped small insects as it oozed out of the trees. In the eighteenth century, the German naturalist, Simon Pallas, leading a scientific exploration of Siberia, was startled to find whole bodies of elephant-like mammoths preserved from decay by the intense cold.

How Fossils are Classified

In the eighteenth century the Swedish botanist Linnaeus devised a method of

Worm tracks and tubes in the rocks at Scarba, Argyllshire

classifying living creatures which worked so well that it is also used for fossils. Its basis is in the idea of species, each of which includes any type of animal, plant or fossil which plainly differs from all other types. Different species which have a general resemblance are grouped in a genus, and there are larger groupings up to the three great kingdoms, animal, vegetable and mineral.

For serious work, a creature, or a fossil, is named by its genus and species, so that a household cat, for example, is *Felix domesticus*. Fortunately we need not always be so precise: you will usually be satisfied with one of the larger groupings. Though a palaeontologist may call a fossil *Terebratula intermedia*, to you it may simply be a lamp-shell. Yet you may find it helpful to know a few of the more common genera, so that, for example, you can distinguish a terebrat from the other lamp-shells.

Plants

Most fossil plants resemble modern ones: there are fossil seaweeds, fossil ferns, fossil flowering plants, and fossil trees, conifers (evergreens) as well as those which shed their leaves in winter. There are also fossil diatoms, plants so small that you need a microscope to see them. Some of the trees which formed coal, though so different from those of today, resemble some of our modern plants grown enormously large.

The Simplest Animals

Whereas most animals, like most plants, consist of multitudinous cells (blobs of living material), the simplest, the protozoa, consist of only one. Many of these unicellular creatures have no solid parts that could get fossilised. Others, tiny as they are, have elaborate skeletons or shells, and so numerous are they that their fossil remains have accumulated to form large rocks. Apart from the diatoms, which are plants, there are two main types of animal protozoa: the solid parts of the radiolaria consist of silica, those of the foraminifera of calcite.

Sponges

Sponges are also called porifera because of the many pores in their bodies through which currents of sea-water supply them with food. Unlike the ordinary household sponge, which consists of horny chitin, fossil sponges consist of silica, calcite or iron. You may find complete sponge "skeletons" or detached spicules, spiky-looking fragments.

Corals

Some marine animals have a very simple structure, consisting of a fleshy tube closed at one end and with a mouth surrounded by a ring of stinging-tentacles at the other. Jelly-fish and sea-anemones are too soft-bodied to be likely to become fossils but, though they resemble sea-anemones, corals have calcite skeletons, and these may accumulate to form great beds of rock.

There are many types of coral. Some are simple, each consisting of one calcite "cup"; others are compound, formed of a number of corallites growing out of one another. All are divided internally by partitions; in the tabulate corals these are horizontal (tabulae); in the rugose corals, which are easy to recognise by the ridges on the outside of their wall, they are vertical (septa).

Graptolites

Graptolites, which are now extinct, had almost as simple a structure; their name means "written on stone", and they do indeed resemble pencil-markings on some very old rocks. They consist of short lengths of chitin, with a row of tiny projections along the edge; in each projection lived a creature something like a coral-animal, and all were connected by a channel of living material along their stipe (stem). It is thought that, when alive, they drifted in the sea, hanging downwards from a central float.

Worms

The many different types of worms are so soft-bodied that you would hardly think them likely to be fossilised. Some of them, however, left grooves where they crawled over mud which has since hardened into rock; some build limy tubes round their bodies and some bore holes even into the hardest rock. These worm-trails, worm-casts and borings are all classed as fossils.

Starfish, Sea-urchins and Sea-lilies

The animals classed as echinoderms (spiny skins) have a thick body-covering which easily gets fossilised; many of them differ from most other animals by having not two sides but a five-fold build to their bodies. The easiest to recognise are the starfish, along with which are classed the feather-stars and brittle-stars. The sea-urchins or echinoids get both names from their spiny tests or shells; one being an old countryside term, and the other Greek for hedgehog. The sea-lilies or crinoids (Greek for lilies) are also named from their appearance, but both terms are misleading, for though these creatures look like plants they are really animals.

Lamp-shells

There are two distinct types of bivalves (two-shelled animals), and these differ completely in body-structure. The brachiopods (arm-feet) are so called because their long projecting fleshy "arm" was once wrongly thought to serve as a foot. It is, in fact, used for directing currents of water towards the body. Some brachiopod shells resemble antique lamps, a hole in the end of a small projecting "beak" looking like the place for the wick —hence the name lamp-shells.

Molluscs

The molluscs (their name is from the Latin *mollis*, soft) are a large and varied group of animals, including some with two shells, some with one shell, and some with no visible shell at all. The bivalve molluscs, the lamellibranchs (layer-gills) are easy to distinguish from the brachiopods:

Brachiopods
The two shells always unequal in size.
Each shell is symmetrical.
Shells are in front, and at the back, of the animal's body.

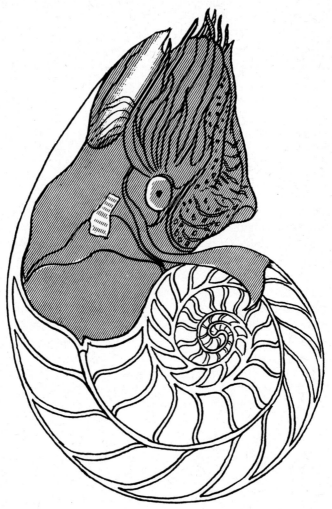

FIGURE 39. *Another modern invertebrate—pearly nautilus*

Shells close when animal dies, so are usually found together.

Shell may have a projecting "beak".

Lamellibranchs

Shells may be equal.

Each shell is asymmetrical.

Shells are at the sides of the body.

Shells open when animal dies, so are often found separately.

Shell has no "beak".

The univalve (single-shelled) molluscs include such gasteropods (stomach-feet) as the winkle, limpet and snail, and those with an internal shell, like the slug.

The most remarkable molluscs are the cephalopods (head-feet). These include the modern octopus, cuttlefish and squid, and an extinct animal somewhat resembling them, the belemnite. They also include the modern spiral-shelled nautilus of the tropical sea, and two extinct animals, the goniatite and ammonite. These animals had shells, mostly spiral, divided into compartments: as they grew they added a larger compartment and moved into it; the rest of the shell, which was almost empty, acted as a float. The three types are distinguished by the shape of the sutures (partitions) separating the compartments: in the nautilus they curve gently; in the goniatite they are wavy or crooked; and in the ammonite they are very complicated, their edges being frilly.

Insects, Spiders, Scorpions and Crustacea

The arthropods (jointed-feet) form a group even more diverse than the molluscs; they include insects and centipedes, spiders and scorpions, and the eurypterids, large extinct sea-scorpions. They also include the crustacea (crusted animals) which are protected by a large hard shell or external skeleton, like crabs and lobsters, and some very interesting extinct animals, the trilobites. Though they look like molluscs, the barnacles or cirripedia (curled-feet), which live in such multitudes on the seashore are really crustaceans. So are the ostracods, whose small bodies are enclosed by limy shells.

The Vertebrates

All the animals mentioned so far are invertebrates—they have no backbones.

Of all the vertebrates (backboned animals) the ones of which you are most likely to find fossils are fish. The others are amphibians, reptiles, birds and mammals (beasts)—which of course include human beings. Fossils of these are not plentiful, but you might possibly come across their teeth or detached bones.

CHAPTER XIV

Reading the Earth's History

ABOUT TWO centuries ago a self-educated canal engineer, William Smith, discovered that each of the rock-beds contains its own special types of fossil. By charting their outcrops, he produced the first geological map of Great Britain, and did more for its geology than the learned men of Europe had done for their countries. Years later, the President of the newly-formed Geological Society hailed him as the father of English geology.

The World's Five Great Eras

Smith's discovery enabled geologists to read the earth's history. They first divided it into two great eras, the Primary and Secondary, but soon they realised that these were not enough. Rock-beds more recent than the Secondary were then called Tertiary, and the most recent of all, containing the first traces of human life, Quaternary. Then, rocks more ancient than those now called Primary needed yet another era. This made the terms Primary and Secondary so misleading that they are falling out of use, although Tertiary and Quaternary are still commonly used.

These five great eras have all been renamed. The very oldest is called the Pre-Cambrian, because all its rocks are older than the most ancient in the next era. This, the former Primary, is now the Palaeozoic; the former Secondary is the Mesozoic; and the Tertiary and Quaternary together form the Cainozoic—from the Greek for ancient, middle and recent life.

Each era is divided into systems. These are almost the same all over the world, but most of the sub-divisions have local names because they vary from place to place, like the Niagara Series and the London Clay. A bed is chiefly formed of one kind of rock, and is divided in zones, each of which contains one special type of fossil found in no other zone.

This zonation of rocks is useful not only to the geologist and fossil-hunter but also to the civil and mining engineer. As soon as you have found and identified the zone fossil, you know for certain just what rock layer you are dealing with, and what sort of rocks are—and what sort are not—to be found below it.

You can also find out roughly how old it is, for there are methods of estimating the age of different rocks. The most accurate method is based on radio-activity; minerals such as uranium gradually turn, at a known rate, into lead, so that the proportion of these minerals in any formation gives a clue to its age.

The Build of Britain

The northern part of Scotland is mostly Pre-Cambrian; south of this is a strip of the Upper Palaeozoic; and still further south is the Lower Palaeozoic. Wales, too, is chiefly Lower Palaeozoic, but there are broad outcrops of Upper Palaeozoic in South Wales.

Except for the Lake District, which is

Lower Palaeozoic, much of the north of England is Upper Palaeozoic, and so are Devon and Cornwall. The rocks in the north-west Midlands are Lower Mesozoic. From the Cotswolds, the Upper Mesozoic beds dip gently towards the south-east. The East Anglian coast, the lower reaches and estuary of the Thames, and the coasts of the Solent and Spithead are Tertiary. The Quaternary covers the floors of many river-valleys and forms small outcrops here and there.

The diversity of the rocks accounts for the varied scenery of Great Britain. Differences in their composition affect the soils they produce, the type of vegetation they grow, and the type of animal they harbour. Divergences in their hardness affect the height and formation of the hills. Variations in their structure affect the appearance of their outcrops. With practice, you will realise how the scenery gives you an idea of the rocks below.

The Build of North America

The geology of North America was first systematically studied last century by the Scottish geologist William Logan, who found that many of its rocks were far older than the so-called Primary. The very oldest are called, because of their shape, the Canadian Shield; it borders on Hudson Bay and its edge is roughly marked by a line of rivers and lakes from the Mackenzie River to the St. Lawrence estuary.

The Shield is bordered in succession by Palaeozoic, Mesozoic and Cainozoic rocks, the former extending southwards from the Great Lakes towards the Gulf of Mexico. The Rockies and Appalachians are mostly of Pre-Cambrian and Palaeozoic age. Along the Atlantic coast the softer Cainozoic rocks continue south towards Florida, while the prairies are largely formed of sheets of loess.

The Pre-Cambrian

Though the Canadian Shield, which has an area of about two million square miles, may be the largest of these great, very ancient outcrops, there are several other Pre-Cambrian shields. They occur in Africa south of the Sahara, around the Baltic, in the east of Siberia, in the southern part of India, in Western Australia and in Antarctica.

These shields were once thought to be the very oldest rocks ever formed, when

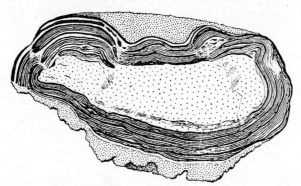

FIGURE 40. *One of the few Pre-Cambrian fossils,* Collenia. *The calcareous layers were probably formed by algae (seaweeds)*

the molten earth grew cold enough for its crust to remain solid. But many of them, being sedimentary, consist of the remains of still older rocks, and even the oldest igneous rocks, being plutonic, welled up from within the earth through rocks older than themselves.

Our earth indeed had a long and varied history before even the most ancient of the Pre-Cambrian rocks began to be formed. During the millions of years needed to form them there were two long-continued earth-movements accompanied by great uprushes of molten rock, and there were also two ice-ages.

There are many smaller Pre-Cambrian outcrops in Britain and America. Being

THE GEOLOGICAL ERAS AND THEIR SYSTEMS

ERAS	DOMINANT FORM OF LIFE	SYSTEMS AND MAIN SUB-DIVISIONS	APPROXIMATE AGES OF THE LOWEST BEDS: MILLION YEARS
QUATERNARY (POST-PLIOCENE)	Human	Holocene (Recent) Pleistocene	one
TERTIARY (CAINOZOIC)	Mammals	Pliocene Miocene Oligocene Eocene	fifteen twenty-five thirty-five sixty
MESOZOIC (SECONDARY)	Reptiles	Cretaceous Chalk Upper Greensand Gault Lower Greensand Wealden Jurassic Colite Lias Rhaetic Triassic	140 170 195
UPPER PALAEOZOIC (PRIMARY)	Fish and Land Plants	Permian Carboniferous Coal-Measures Millstone Grit Mountain Limestone Devonian and Old Red Sandstones	220 275 320
LOWER PALAEOZOIC (PRIMARY)	Invertebrates	Silurian Ordovician Cambrian	350 420 520
PRE-CAMBRIAN	Hardly any	—	3,000

so old, they are very hard; they produce some of the finest scenery: lofty mountains, steep-sided hills and rugged cliffs. Many of them contain valuable minerals; gold, iron, copper, nickel, chromium and uranium. While enjoying the wildness of the very resistant rocks you can study the effects made on them by the weather, the rivers and the sea, and in them you will find interesting mineral specimens to collect.

Was there Life in Pre-Cambrian Times?

But you may search in vain among the Pre-Cambrian rocks for the remains of living creatures. They contain very few fossils, hardly any of which are recognizable except by an experienced palaeontologist. These are mostly worm-casts and borings, and masses of doubtful material which may or may not have been formed by living things; if they were, they have altered so much that all trace of their original structure is lost.

Why these ancient rocks should be so barren, when the very oldest Cambrian rocks are so fossiliferous, is not clear. The palaeontologists have not yet been able to work this problem out. Probably, the animals living in those distant times had no parts (such as shells) hard enough to become fossilised.

CHAPTER XV

The Age of Ancient Life

THE ROCKS William Smith studied were mostly in England. The Welsh rocks, which were much older, were far more difficult to understand, and for some time the geologists simply called them grauwacke—a word, meaning greystone, coined by A. G. Werner the German geologist—and left it at that. They were not systematically investigated until 1831. Then two geologists undertook the task. Adam Sedgwick, a Yorkshireman, started with the very oldest, in North Wales, and classed them as the Cambrian System, after the Celtic name for Wales.

His friend, the Scots geologist Roderick Impey Murchison, began studying what he called the "interminable grauwacke", where it underlay the more recent outcrops of South Wales. Using the name of a Welsh tribe which had lived in that region, he called them the Silurian System.

As Sedgwick worked his way upwards through the Cambrian beds and Murchison worked downwards through the Silurian, they were bound to meet somewhere, and each claimed the middlemost rocks for his own system. The bitter dispute that followed was settled only when, in 1879, Charles Lapworth classed these rocks as a separate system, naming it after another Welsh tribe, the Ordovician.

The Lower Palaeozoic

The three systems, which together form the Lower Palaeozoic, include very hard shales, limestones and sandstone, most of which were originally sediments formed in a great ocean trough which extended across the Atlantic. In Ordovician times it began to buckle, and there were other earth movements and much volcanic action; in the Silurian the movements

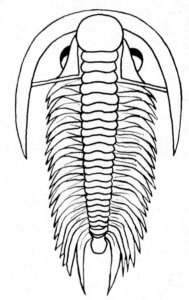

FIGURE 41. *A trilobite*—Baradoxides

were more gentle and the trough silted up.

Trilobites

The most interesting Lower Palaeozoic fossils are the trilobites, named from the three lobes, separated by grooves, which form their bodies. So different are they from any modern animals that the early palaeontologists showed their perplexity by giving them such names as *Paradoxides* (seemingly impossible), *Agnostus* (unknown), and *Cryptolithus* (mysterious stone).

The quarrymen, who were just as puzzled, simply called them "Dudley bugs".

Though some of the trilobites do certainly look like weird, giant insects, they are not insects at all. They are arthropods, very distantly related to the spiders; among their modern relatives are the king-crabs, which are unlike ordinary crabs and are not found in British waters.

The trilobites' soft bodies were protected by external skeletons of chitin and calcite; when they grew too large for their covering they shed it and grew another. Hence you are more likely to find separate parts of the cast-off skeletons—a head-shield, a tail-shield, or a segmented body-shield—than complete ones; some are so

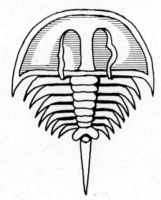

FIGURE 42. *A fossil king-crab*

hard that they stand out in relief from the softer rock-surfaces.

Lower Palaeozoic Brachiopods

In these rocks lamp-shells and other brachiopods are plentiful, much more so than bivalve molluscs. One, *Lingula*, though it may not be the most ancient type of animal to survive to modern times, is certainly the oldest type known. Its oval shells are almost the same size and, though they are very thin, the animal within them is so hardy that it lives even when the mud it burrows into is uncovered by the tide or full of decaying material; if

buried by a mass of silt that would kill most animals, *Lingula* simple tunnels its way out.

The small Cambrian brachiopod *Obolus* is named after the ancient Greek coin which it resembles. The shell of *Orthis*, in the Ordovician, is almost square, with a straight single-line. Two Silurian types are large, with bulging shells and a curved "beak": *Conchidium* is distinguishable from *Pentamerus* by being more deeply-grooved.

Lower Palaeozoic Corals

Corals are found in the Ordovician but are more plentiful in the Silurian. Of the rugose (wrinkled) types, *Omphyma* is simple; shaped something like a child's top,

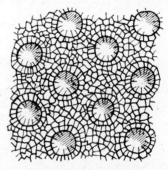

FIGURE 43. *A Lower Palaeozoic Coral*—Heliolites, *magnified to show corallites*

perhaps with downgrowths like roots. *Kodonophyllum* is a compound rugose coral; its septa meet at its centre.

Some of the compound tabulate corals are *Favosites*, with six-sided corallites, fitting closely together like a honeycomb. *Heliolites* also consist of small close-fitting corallites, among which some large cylindrical ones form a pattern. The corallites of *Syringopora* are separated slightly but are connected by horizontal side-growths. Those of *Halysites* look like a thin chain crossing the limestone.

Graptolites

There are several types of "rock-writing" animals, graptolites. In the Cambrian, the dendroid (tree-like) graptolites have several stems, branching out irregularly. The Ordovician *Tetragraptus* has four stems; the "tuning fork" graptolite, *Didymograptus*, has two, side by side: *Diplograptus* one, with the cups on both sides. The Silurian *Monograptus* is also single-stemmed, but has cups only on one side; it may be straight, curved or spiral.

Lower Palaeozoic Echinoderms

The Echinoderms of the Lower Palaeo-

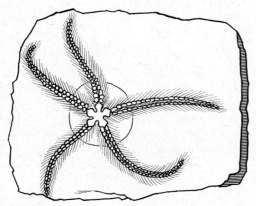

FIGURE 44. *A Lower Palaeozoic echinoderm—brittle-star*

lithic include an extinct type, the cystids, which were not five-sided but pear-shaped, with a holdfast securing them to the rocks. The Silurian rocks of Shropshire contain fossil starfish and fragments of brittle-stars, whose long feathery-looking, spine-fringed arms really were brittle.

Sea-lilies began in the Lower Ordovician and were plentiful in the Silurian. You are most likely to find detached portions of their long stems, but if you are lucky, you may find complete specimens, looking like outlandish plants with their flower-like bodies, their long stems, and their holdfasts. You may even find a sea-lily colony, resembling a fossilised flower-bed.

Lower Palaeozoic Molluscs

Molluscs were not abundant in the Lower Palaeozoic, and you are less likely to find their actual shells than their moulds and casts, some of them deformed by earth-movements. The oldest Cambrian gasteropods are uncoiled; but *Bellerophon*, in the Upper Cambrian, has a coiled shell.

Lower Palaeozoic Cephalopods

Cephalopod fossils are found in all the systems from the Upper Cambrian onwards. In Palaeozoic times, the food of cephalopods probably consisted of trilobites, but, whereas the shell of the modern cephalopods is spiral, those of the early types had many strange shapes. *Meloceras*, also called *Cyrtoceras*, had a shell which curved like a horn; *Orthoceras* was almost straight; *Gyroceras'* was an "open" spiral; and that of *Ophidioceras* was a spiral whose coils touched but did not fit tightly together.

Other Lower Palaeozoic Fossils

The earliest sea-mats occur in the Ordovician; some form a covering to fossil shells, others are hard to distinguish from corals. You may find burrows and trails of sea-worms, or the spiral coils of the worm-tube *Spirorbis*, which you might mistake for the shell of a mollusc.

The *Stromatoporoids*, of the Ordovician and Silurian, form masses of material in wavy concentric layers connected by rod-like growths; in some ways they resemble corals, in others foraminifera, and in others seaweeds. A microscope is needed to distinguish the protozoa and the loose sponge-spicules. Except near the top of the Silurian the only Lower Palaeozoic plants are the seaweeds.

Grikes in the mountain limestone—Malham Cove, Yorkshire

The Upper Palaeozoic

Life in Lower Palaeozoic times was limited almost entirely to the sea; even there it consisted almost entirely of invertebrate (backboneless) animals. Only towards the end of the period did fish appear in the sea and life spread on to land.

Conditions in the Upper Palaeozoic were very different. Fish were abundant in the sea, and dense forests grew on the land, where numerous types of animals also lived. Some of the rocks of this part of the era resemble those below them, but others are quite different.

The Devonian and Old Red Sandstone

Before they worked in Wales, Sedgwick and Murchison visited Scotland in 1826 to study the Old Red Sandstone (called the Old Red or even the O.R.S. for short). As this was thought to be unfossiliferous, they were very excited when they found it contained some fossil fish.

Their work was continued by Hugh Miller, a stone-mason's apprentice who was so deeply interested by the fossils he found in the quarries that he educated himself and became one of Britain's foremost palaeontologists. His book *The Old Red Sandstone* is very interesting and forms a useful guide to the subject.

In 1835, Sedgwick and Murchison started examining the West Country. They decided that though its rocks resemble those in the Silurian its fossils are so very different that it was really a more recent system, the Devonian. It forms two main areas in Great Britain: one, including Exmoor, is in North Devon; the other builds much of South Devon and Cornwall.

Although the Devonian and the O.R.S. are so different in type of rock and in the scenery they produce that they are classed as two different systems, they were formed at about the same time and are the lowest Upper Palaeozoic beds. The Devonian mostly consists of limestones, shales and sandstones, deposited on the floor of a sea which extended across southern England into Belgium.

The Old Red is so dark a sandstone that it gives the soils above it a ruddy hue. It accumulated on the floors of a number of lochs separated by mountain ranges trending north-east to south-west; these were produced by powerful earth movements which occurred about the end of

the Silurian. These rocks are found not only in Scotland but in South Wales, the northern part of Europe, and the eastern part of North America.

Armoured Fish

The earliest fossil fish are found in the Upper Silurian Beds, and they are less plentiful in the Devonian than in the O.R.S., where they are abundant. Some resembled the sharks but, as their skeletons consisted not of bone but of gristle, the only parts of them which you are likely to find are their teeth.

Most of these early fish were very different from modern ones, but they slightly resembled the sturgeon. Their scales were very large, some being three inches long, two inches wide, and over an eighth of an inch thick; and, as they were covered with a shining enamel, these fish are called ganoids from the Greek for brightness.

Some of the ganoid fish were about eight feet long and had great shields covering their heads. The shield of *Cephalaspis* extended for about a third of its length. In spite of its name, *Pterichthys* (winged fish) was not a flying-fish like those of today; its four fins may not even have been used for swimming but simply to cross the sandy sea-floor when it got stranded at low tide. Some of these early fish, like the modern lung-fish, may even have been able to live for a time out of water. *Osteolepis*, which had smaller scales and no head-shield, resembled the type from which land-living vertebrates are thought to be descended.

Sea-scorpions

Of the many invertebrates which lived in Devonian and Old Red times, the strangest were the *Eurypterids*, the sea-scorpions. These first appear in the Cambrian rocks of America, but the oldest

Fossil head—shield of ganoid fish (Cephalaspis)

British specimens are found in the Silurian. Towards the end of that period they got really large, some of them being over six feet long.

Like the trilobites, the sea-scorpions were arthropods, and their bodies were similarly protected by an external skeleton divided into segments. It tapered towards the tail, which was broad and flat in the

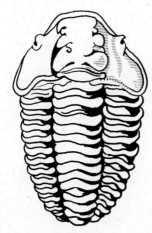

FIGURE 45. *The Dudley Bug*, Calymene

swimming types and long and pointed in the burrowers. Hugh Miller thought that their shields looked something like those carried by mediaeval knights; their markings resemble those which sculptors carve on the wings of stone angels, so the Scottish quarrymen rather profanely called these fossils "Seraphim".

Other Devonian and O.R.S. Fossils

The trilobites of the period resemble those of the Silurian, but were not so plentiful. They include *Calymene*, the "Dudley Bug". Sea-lilies are found in the Devonian and O.R.S., and sea-urchins are more abundant than in the rocks below. Many brachiopods, too, occur in these beds, and the large *Stringocephalus*, almost circular except for its straight hinge-line and its prominent pointed "beak", is

found only in them. *Spirifer* is broad and almost butterfly-shaped.

The lamellibranchs include *Nucula*, with a rounded triangular shell; *Cardiola*, whose shell bears two sets of markings, one from the centre of the hinge and the other parallel to the oval edge; *Concardium*, with its triangular shell projecting something like a tube; and the large thick-shelled *Megaladon* with its toothed hinge. The gasteropod *Euomphalus* has a shell which is a flattish spiral, and *Bellerophon* is also found in these beds.

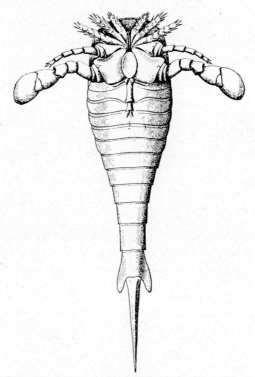

FIGURE 46. *The under surface of a sea-scorpion—Eurypterus*

Some Devonian limestones are very rich in corals, which are easier to see if you damp the surface of the rock; near Torquay and Newton Abbot are large bands of coral reef. Most of the types are similar to the Silurian, but one interesting coral, *Calceola*, has an operculum, a sort of "lid".

Corals in carboniferous limestone—Ravenstonedale, Westmorland

Only a few graptolites are to be found; they had almost all died out in the Silurian. There were several types of nautilus, and ammonites had appeared.

Coral (lithostration in carboniferous limestone)—Castlemartin, Pembrokeshire

The plants were much like those which afterwards grew in the great coal-forests.

Mountain Limestone

Although its name means "coal-bearing", only the uppermost rocks in the next system, the Carboniferous, form the actual coal-measures. The Lower Carboniferous consists largely of a limestone so hard that it stands out as hills when the softer rocks have weathered away. Hence the Carboniferous limestone is also the Mountain Limestone; in America, rocks of this period form the Mississippian System and contain some coal.

This limestone accumulated in a shallow sea which swept across much of Britain, "drowning" and merging into one the inland seas whose sediments formed the Old Red Sandstone. In England, the ridges between them mostly weathered away, so that here the Lower Carboniferous consists almost entirely of limestone. Further north, they were not completely destroyed, and material washed from their slopes made the sea turbid; it hardened into sandstones and shales, while swamp-forests along the shore became seams of coal.

These beds cross Scotland obliquely and underlie the great central plain of Ireland. They also build such hills as the Pennines, the Mendips, and Wenlock Edge; in Somerset and in Derbyshire they are trenched by gorges, such as Cheddar, and by thickly-wooded dales.

Above the mountain limestone the surface is almost waterless; seeping down into the rock, the rain excavates caves and swallow-holes. In Yorkshire, it is traversed by deep grooves called grikes. Where these grooves are deeper and wider and extend over a wider area, as in Jugoslavia and the south-eastern part of the United States, they produce a strange scenery, the karst.

Carboniferous Corals

Like other limestones, this rock is rich in fossils, including some interesting corals. The septa of *Lithostrothion* are alternately long and short, with a central columella; its corallites may be cylindrical and branch out tree fashion or, as in *Lithostrotion basaltiforme*, they may be crowded together something like the basalt pillars in the Giant's Causeway. In *Lonsdaleia*, the septa are not long enough to reach the outer "wall".

The simple coral *Zaphrentis* forms a curved cone, resembling an old-fashioned drinking-horn; it may be about an inch long and its broader end may be half an inch across. *Caninia* is somewhat similar, but larger; it is longer in proportion to its width, and may be cylindrical instead of conical.

Carboniferous Sea-lilies

Crinoids, too, abound in the Carboni-

ferous limestone. Great masses of rock in the Peak District are full of "screwstones", detached portions of crinoidal stems; when polished this encrinital limestone forms an ornamental stone, wrongly called "marble". You may also find sea-lily heads, or complete specimens, singly or in colonies.

A little Greek will help you to identify some of the sea-lilies. The head of *Amphoracrinus* looks something like an antique wine-jar (amphora); *Rhodocrinus* means rose lily and *Cupressocrinus* means cypress lily. With projections from its

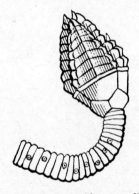

FIGURE 47. *A lower Carboniferous sea-lily*—Cupressocrinus, *showing head and part of stem*

stem like short stumpy branches *Actinocrinus* (rayed lily) is even more plant-like than the other crinoids.

Carboniferous Brachiopods

One of the brachiopods in the mountain limestone is *Productus*, whose shell is broad compared with its length and is crisscrossed with closely-set grooves. On some specimens you may notice rounded spots or even short projections; these are the stumps of long spines, which are thought to have enabled the living animal to cling on to the sea-lily stems. Others are the butterfly-like *Spirifer*, and *Rhynchonella* whose shell is oval or triangular with rounded corners.

Carboniferous Molluscs

The Carboniferous lamellibranchs include *Modiola*, resembling the mussel but more oblong; *Conocordium* and *Posidonia* with lop-sided shells; *Nucula* and *Leda*, roughly triangular or oval; and *Edmondia* with concentric markings or ridges. The gasteropods include *Bellerophon* and *Euomphalus* and *Pleurotomaria* with zigzag markings. They also include *Orthoceras* and other types of nautilus. Some of the goniatites are so large you would find them difficult to lift.

King-crabs and Sea-scorpions

During this period the trilobites were dying out. Its crustaceans, however, include king-crabs and sea-scorpions, as well as ostracods, whose tiny shells resemble those of the modern *Cypris* which naturalists find in ditches and streams.

Sea-mats were then so plentiful that, in places, the limestone seems to be almost completely made of them; where it is weather-worn they stand out in relief like a lacy covering. Other layers of the rock largely consist of microscopic foraminifera. Remains of fish are rather scarce, but detached scales and teeth are sometimes found.

The Farewell Rock

The base of the Upper Carboniferous is formed by the Millstone Grit: its layers of conglomerate and pebbly sandstone are so gritty (coarse-grained) that they make splendid grinding-stones for windmills. This rock consists of hardened sediment from the delta of a great river that flowed southwards from a land covering what is now Scotland and the regions nearby. Miners call it the *Farewell Rock* because when they see it they know that it marks the end of the coal-bearing rocks. It is not very fossiliferous but some goniatites are found.

FIGURE 48. *Another sea-lily*—Actinocrinus

Coral bed in carboniferous limestone—Treflach Wood, Shropshire

Mummified Vegetation

As the delta silted up it became a vast swamp little above sea-level. Across it spread great forests and, as the ground slowly sank beneath them, they were buried time and again by fresh masses of sediment brought down by the river from the north.

Hardening under the weight of the growing accumulations of sediment, the mud of the swamps became sandstone and shale; the ooze on their surface became fire-clay; the decaying vegetation from the forests charred—you might almost say "mummified"—and became the seams of coal.

The whole series of rocks—the sandstones and shales with the coal-seams between them—forms the greater part of the Upper Carboniferous. In Britain they are called the coal-measures but, in America, rocks of the same age, equally rich in coal, are classed as a separate system, the Pennsylvanian.

The beds below the coal-seams contain tree-roots, and the beds above them contain the trunks of trees which were buried by the accumulating mud before they had time to fall. As their interiors decayed, sediment which seeped in to fill them hardened, and the trunks became cylinders of sandstone, slightly wider at their base, and surrounded by a thin layer of coal which was once their bark.

The Coal-forests

On the surface of slabs of coal (or of the shale from the coal-measures) you may find impressions of some of the trees which produced it. You will notice how very different they were from the trees of today; they are much more like some modern

123

plants and shrubs grown to enormous proportions.

Lepidodendron (scaly tree) resembled a huge club-moss; its branches were thickly

Marine fossils in the shales show that the sea sometimes submerged the coal-forests: the brachiopods include *Spirifer*, *Productus* and *Lingula*. The lamellibranchs

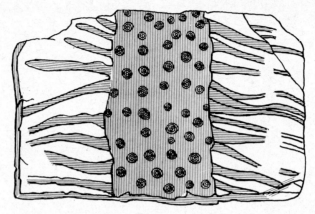

FIGURE 49. *A fossil tree from the coal-measures*—Sigillaria

set with tiny leaves and ended in large cones: as the leaves fell off they left the scaly pattern from which the tree is named. In *Sigillaria* (seal-like) the marks left by the fallen leaves resemble the imprint of legal seals; its branching roots were once thought to come from a different type of tree called (from its appearance) *Stigmaria* (stain-like).

The *Pteridosperms* (ferny seeds) were trees like seed-bearing ferns with leaves in feathery fronds several inches across. *Calamites* (reed-like) looked something like horse-tails, but were up to sixty feet high. The *Sphenophyllia* (wedge-leaves) were climbing plants using the great trees as supports.

Other Coal-measure Fossils

In the coal-measures too, are the fossils of insects that lived in those great forests: mayflies, termites, cockroaches, locusts, crickets and giant dragon-flies with a two-foot wing-span. Other land-living creatures included scorpions much like those of today.

include such marine types as *Aviculopecten*, perhaps with a brassy-looking coating of iron pyrites, and *Posidonia*, a thin shell with concentric markings, as well as fresh-water types like *Carbonicola*. Goniatites

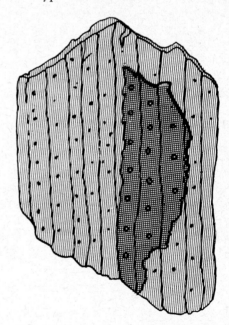

FIGURE 50. *Another fossil tree*—Stigmaria

are more plentiful than nautilus and ammonites.

The fossils of the period include fish. But the most interesting are those of the amphibians, its only land vertebrates. Some resembled crocodiles but were more clumsy; others had squat heads almost half as long as their bodies: others were squat and bulky. The *Labyrinthodonts* (maze-toothed) are so called because of the complicated structure of their teeth.

The New Red Sandstone

A period of mountain-building which followed the Carboniferous produced several anticlines and synclines. Much of the coal-measures was destroyed by the weather, those in the synclines remaining as the coal-fields. Divided by the anti-

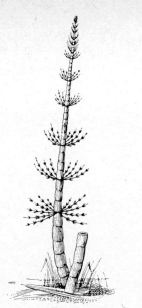

FIGURE 51. *Carboniferous horsetail*—Calamites

Trunk and roots of club-moss—Hampton Pit, Staffordshire

clinal ridges, the sea became a number of inland lakes and, as these dried up, they became sandy wastes.

The rocks produced by these wastes form part of the New Red Sandstone, which has a much lighter colour than the O.R.S. They contain few fossils but there are

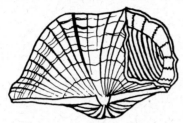

FIGURE 52. Spirifer trigonalis

enough of these to show that its rocks belong not only to two geological systems but to two distinct geological eras.

The Permian System

The lower New Red Sandstone, together with a thick bed of dolomite (magnesian limestone) were called by Murchison the Permian System after the Russian province where he studied it. The limestone itself is named from the Dolomites, part of the Italian Alps; its main English outcrop extends from the Durham coast almost to Nottingham.

Most of the Permian fossils are found in the magnesian limestone, masses of it consisting of polyzoa. During this period, the trilobites and sea-scorpions died out, but the vertebrates included not only fish and amphibians but the earliest reptiles. One of the world's great geological eras was ending, and its living creatures were beginning to resemble those of the next.

CHAPTER XVI

The Age of Middle Life

THOUGH THE rocks above the Permian form the base of the Mesozoic, they too consist of light red pebble-beds, marls and sandstones, and they too are part of the New Red Sandstone. Indeed, it is hard to distinguish the one series from the other, for the same desert conditions prevailed during both.

But though the rocks of the two series are so similar, the fossils they contain are very different indeed. The plants of the new period were still mostly cycads, conifers and ferns, but its animals show that this really was the beginning of the Age of Middle Life. No longer were there any graptolites, trilobites, or sea-scorpions;

The petrified Forest of Arizona (formed during the Triassic Period)

but there were giant reptiles who left their footprints and their skeletons in the rocks: the Mesozoic is the Age of Reptiles.

The Trias

The lowest Mesozoic beds are called the

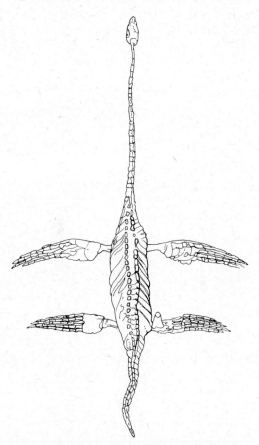

FIGURE 53. *The skeleton of* Plesiosaurus

Trias because in Germany, where they were first studied, they contain three different types of rock. In Britain there are only two, the Bunter (mottled) Pebble-beds below the Keuper marls; in Germany, they are separated by the *Muschelkalk*, a deep-sea formation which yields most of the Triassic fossils.

The main English outcrop extends from the Severn into the Midlands and along both sides of the Pennines. In Cheshire,

it contains the great beds of rock-salt; the "Tea Green Marls" of the Somerset coast near Watchet also belong to this system.

The White Lias

Fossils, so sparse in most Triassic rocks, are plentiful in its upper bed, the Rhaetic, named after a region in the Alps. In England, where this forms a ridge from the Devonshire coast near Lyme Regis to the Yorkshire coast south of the Tees, it is also called white lias because it contains a bed of white limestone as well as some shales and grey marls.

The Rhaetic was formed when a sea flooded the Triassic salt-lakes and deserts. Remains of the animals it drowned are found in a fossiliferous "Bone Bed" bordering the Severn Estuary. They include the fossil of the first British mammal, *Microlestes*.

The Blue Lias

Miss Anning as a child ne'er passed
A pin upon the ground;
But picked it up, and so at last
An ichthyosaurus found.

These lines praised, as an example to other children, a carpenter's daughter of Lyme Regis. Mary Anning, early in the nineteenth century, used to search the foreshore for the queer-looking stones which visitors bought as curios. Some of the visitors were palaeontologists, and they so much interested her in the fossils that she too became a geologist and started a systematic hunt for them. This was so successful that her work is commemorated in a stained glass window in a Lyme Regis church.

She found the *Ichthyosaurus* skeleton—the first reasonably complete one—when she was only eleven. Later, she found the first complete skeleton of a *Plesiosaurus* and that of the first British *Pterosaurus*.

The rocks which yielded them are the Blue Lias, the lowest part of the Jurassic System, named after the Jura Mountains. Its "layers" are alternate beds of dark blue shale and pale blue limestone, deposited on the floor of a sea which

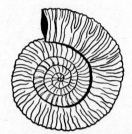

FIGURE 54. *The ammonite* Hildoceras

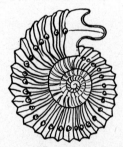

FIGURE 55. *The ammonite* Dactyloceras

FIGURE 56. *The ammonite* Asteroceras

covered much of England, though why they have this strange alternation is unknown.

The Giant Reptiles

Some of the giant Mesozoic reptiles lived in the sea; the *Ichthyosaurus* (fish lizard) looked like a fish, though it was really a stream-lined marine reptile. Another was the long-necked *Plesiosaurus* (almost lizard). Other Liassic reptiles lived on land or at the water's edge: *Steneosaurus* (narrow lizard), for example, resembled a large crocodile.

The *Pterosaurus* (winged lizard) which Mary Anning discovered was a flying reptile. Although webbed, its wings were very different from those of a bat; they extended from its "little" finger to the side of its body. It may not have been able to soar from the ground; aided by its clawed fingers, it probably climbed the trees and then swooped down, glider-fashion, on its prey.

Liassic Ammonites

Though you may come across the bones or teeth of such reptiles, the fossils you are more likely to find in the Blue Lias are those of the cephalopods: not goniatites but nautilus and many types of ammonite. The latter got their name because the early collectors of "figured stones" thought that these spiral shells looked something like the horns which the sculptors of old used to put, as a sign of power, on the heads of statues of the god Jupiter-Ammon.

Some Liassic ammonite shells have a number of projections (*Lytoceras*); some are smooth or nearly so (*Phylloceras*); some are flattened, with a prominent "keel" along the centre-line of their rim (*Harpoceras*); some have a larger centre and a groove along each side of the keel (*Hildoceras*); and some have prominent "ribs" (*Asteroceras*).

"Thunderbolts"

Modern cuttlefish have a "bone", the flaky white material which bird-lovers put in their pets' cages. The pencil-like grey objects, almost cylindrical but pointed at one end, found in the Lias, are the fossil "bones" of extinct cuttlefish. The country

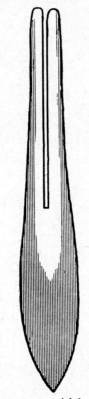

FIGURE 57. *A belemnite*

name for these fossils used to be "thunderbolts", and their scientific name, belemnites, comes from the Greek for dart.

The grey object is not the actual shell: it is the guard which protected the belemnite's internal shell. This was a delicate calcite cone, different from an ammonite shell in that it was straight instead of curved and inside the body instead of out. Specimens of the cone itself are less common, but some have been found complete with a fossil ink-sac like that of a modern squid.

Other Liassic Fossils

In the Lias the brachiopods *Rhynchonella*

and *Terebratula* may also be found. Its lamellibranchs include *Hippopodium ponderosum*, the large flat *Pecten*, *Lima*, *Ostraea* and the "Devil's Toe-nail" *Gryphaea*. One of the most common gasteropods is *Pleurtomaria*, whose spiral shell forms a cone. Corals are rather scarce, but some occur in the limestone. In all the Liassic rocks there are sharks' teeth and fossils of fish or of the lobster-like *Eryon* to be found.

The Lower Oolite

The upper part of the Jurassic is called the Oolite, most of its limestone having a

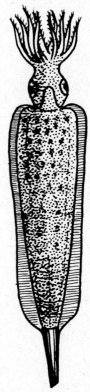

FIGURE 58. *A belemnite showing the internal shell (phragmacone)*

coarse granular texture like fish roe. Though softer than the mountain limestone, this rock is hard enough to build ranges of hills: the Cotswolds and their continuations to north and south, and the

Shelly jurassic limestone at Helmesdale, Sutherland

North Yorkshire moors. It dips gently towards the south-east, ending on the north-west in a steep scarp. It mostly accumulated on the floor of sandy lagoons formed by slight earth movements but, in Yorkshire, these movements produced swampy estuaries.

Giant Plant-eaters

The giant reptiles of Oolitic times include *Ophthalmosaurus* (eyed lizard) resembling a toothless ichthyosaur and *Pliosaurus* resembling a plesiosaur but with a shorter neck. *Megalosaurus* (great lizard) was a flesh-eater about thirty feet long; the vegetarian *Ceteosaurus* (whale lizard) is named simply from its bulk.

Even larger are the gigantic dinosaurs (terrible lizards) found in North America. The very largest were plant-eaters, so huge that they may have lived under water, raising their heads on their long necks to breathe and to browse on the vegetation growing by the water-side: *Brontosaurus* (thunder lizard) was over fifty feet long; *Diplodocus* and *Atlantosaurus* measured nearly a hundred feet. The back and tail of the smaller *Stegosaurus* (armoured lizard) were protected by huge bony plates and spikes, some over a yard high.

Other dinosaurs were flesh-eaters and though smaller than the huge vegetarians were yet quite large. Some, like *Tyrannosaurus*, had very powerful hind-legs, so that they moved something after the style of kangaroos, using their small forelegs as arms.

Other reptiles were quite tiny and lived upon insects. *Schleromochlus* was less than nine inches long and is thought to have moved in jumps. There were also several types of the winged pterosaurs.

Other Oolitic Fossils

The invertebrate fossils of the Oolite are

also interesting. They include belemnite and nautilus shells, and ammonites, such as *Ludwigia* with a smooth shell and *Stephanoceros* with broad whorls and well-marked ribs. They also include the brachiopods *Terebratula* and *Rhynchonella*; the lamellibranchs *Lima*, *Trigonia* and *Ostrea*; and the gasteropod *Nerinea*.

Fossil sea-urchins are plentiful: some are flattish and circular or five-sided (*Clypeus*) and others more rounded (*Holectypus*). One of the commonest sea-lilies, *Apiocrinus*, is almost pear-shaped. All the Mesozoic corals are *Hexacoralla*: unlike the Palaeozoic ones they have six well-marked

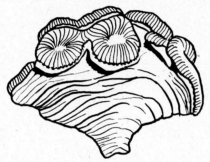

FIGURE 59. *The Middle Oolitic fossil* Thecosimilia

septa. Coral reefs were built in the Jurassic lagoons by simple corals like *Montlivaltia*, which is conical or cylindrical, and the compound *Isastraea* and *Thamnasteria*, whose corallites are packed so tightly together that they become polygons.

The Middle Oolite

After these rocks were formed, currents made the sea turbid, so that the Middle Oolite includes many clay beds. One, the Oxford Clay, contains many fossils, some squeezed out of shape and others showing the brassy gleam of iron pyrites. They include ammonites, belemnites, and large *Gryphaea* shells.

The coral rag, a coarse, hard limestone found in the south of England and Yorkshire, may have been formed when earth

movements raised a ridge which cut off the flow of muddy water from the north. Its fossils include the coral *Thecosimilia*, the small lamellibranch *Exogyra*, and the sea-urchins *Cidaris* and *Hemicidaris*. In the Midlands, a black or grey clay of the same age as the rag contains *Ostraea*, a fossil oyster.

The Upper Oolite

The uppermost Oolite bed to extend right across England south-east of the Cotswolds is the Kimmeridge Clay, dark, shaly, and including layers of clayey limestone and nodules (rounded lumps) of hardened clay. Near its top is a layer of oil-shale which can be used as fuel but produces an unpleasant smoke. In the clay are ammonites, *Exogyra*, *Ostraea*, and scattered bones of *Ichthyosaurus* and *Plesiosaurus*.

Further earth movements produced a sheltered gulf which extended from the south of England into north-west France; the sediment on its floor hardened into rocks found nowhere else. These Portland Beds are best seen on the Dorset coast and near Boulogne; but they are also found inland as far north as Aylesbury.

If you walk up the main street of Portland you will see a notice: *Fossil Garden*; here a stone-quarrying firm displays the interesting fossils which its workmen have found in the Portland stone. This is a limestone much used for building and containing the lamellibranchs *Ostraea*, *Cardium*, *Pecten* and *Trigonia*; and the gasteropod *Cerithium*. The name of some of its ammonites is explained by their size, *Gigantites giganteus*.

Earth movements later reduced the size of the gulf, so that the Purbeck Beds were formed, some in fresh water, others beneath the sea, others in estuaries. The "Dirt Beds", accumulated on dry land, consist of a former soil containing the fossilised stumps of cycads. The "Fossil Forest" on the cliffs above Lulworth Cove grew in one of these ancient soils, and another bed, at Durlston Bay, contains the fossils of some small mammals.

A more recent layer, called from its appearance the "Cinder Bed", contains *Ostraea* and the sea-urchin *Hemicideris*. It was formed beneath the sea, as was another

FIGURE 60.   Paludina *limestone, the so-called Purbeck limestone*

higher bed containing the small lamellibranch *Corula*, but between these marine formations are layers of freshwater limestone. Higher still is the so-called "Purbeck Marble", an ornamental greenish rock whose correct name, taken from the gasteropod fossils in which it abounds, is Paludina Limestone.

Bird-reptile or Reptile-bird?

One fossil found in the Jurassic beds is especially interesting. Only two specimens of it are known, both having been found in the lithographic stone (a limestone formerly used in printing) of Bavaria. *Archaeopteryx* (ancient wing) was part reptile and part bird: about the size of a pigeon, it had teeth and a long tail, and claws on its fore-limbs—but these fore-limbs were not legs but wings, and these and its long tail were lined with feathers. Does it surprise you that a bird should resemble a reptile? Then you have not noticed the scales on the legs of a hen!

The Cretaceous System

Above the Jurassic rocks, and with the same general south-easterly dip, comes the Cretaceous (from the Latin for chalky) System. In England it stretches from the Dorset coast to Salisbury Plain, along the Chilterns, roughly parallel to the Cotswolds, to the Norfolk Coast; further north, it reappears as the Lincolnshire and Yorkshire Wolds; and it forms the North and South Downs and the backbone of the Isle of Wight.

The Wealden Series

Several of its beds are below the chalk: you might think of the Wealden series in south-eastern England as either the uppermost bed of the Jurassic or as the base of the Lower Cretaceous. Its fossils are much like those in the Purbeck Beds, but show that the lagoon had become a freshwater lake. They include the gasteropod *Paludina*, the lamellibranch *Cyrena*; and *Estheria* which, although it has two shells, is not a mollusc but a small crustacean. On the south-west coast of the Isle of Wight is the "Pine Raft", containing the drifted remains of many coniferous trees.

The Greensand and Gault

William Smith found the sand in a cretaceous outcrop so brightly stained with glauconite that he called it greensand. Elsewhere it splits into two separate beds

Fossil tree-trunk in Purbeck Beds—Portisham Quarry

Fossil oyster-bed in Portland Stone—Collingfield Quarry, Portland, Dorset

Cardinia, *a fossil lamellibranch—Thealby Mine, Lincs.*

divided by clay, and varies greatly in composition. For this reason a rock called the Lower Greensand is only exceptionally green, in many places it is not even a sand, and it forms the loftiest hills in the south-east of England!

Its base is the fossiliferous Atherfield clay, containing a "Bone Bed" yielding many fish-bones and a "Perna Bed" yielding many lamellibranchs. In Yorkshire, however, the corresponding bed is the Speeton clay, rich in ammonites and belemnites.

The layer of blue clay which separates the two layers of the greensand is called gault. It gives its ammonites a mother-of-pearl lustre; one, whose shell is partly uncurled, is *Hamites*.

The Upper Greensand, which in some places forms a thin layer at the base of the chalk, is not so fossiliferous.

White, Grey and Red Chalk

The chalk, like the globigerina ooze of the sea-floor which it so much resembles, consists almost completely of organic material and microscopic fossils, *Globigerina* being one of the Protozoa. The chalk, however, was formed not in the ocean but in shallower seas which then covered most of England and north-west France. Where the water was turbid, instead of being clear, the chalk is not white but grey; the red chalk of Hunstanton in Norfolk is stained with iron.

The flints in the chalk consist of silica and the marcasite of iron. Both are of organic origin, though why they should accumulate in these rounded nodules is not yet known.

Loaves, Hearts, Mitres and Crowns

Except for those in the flints, which are

almost black, the chalk fossils are creamy white. They are so many sea-urchins that the countryfolk have given them names: the rounded ones, *Echinocorys*, are fairy loaves; the flattened ones, *Micraster*, *Holaster* and *Hemiaster*, are fairy hearts; and the taller pointed ones, *Conulus* and *Calerites*, are shepherds' mitres or shepherds' crowns. Sea-lilies are less common;

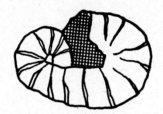

FIGURE 61. *The chalk ammonite* Scaphites

worm *Serpula*, as well as many ostracods.

You should find sponges both in the chalk and in the flints: *Ventriculites* may be funnel-shaped, cup-shaped or cylindrical; *Doryderma* is cylindrical or pear-shaped. A flint's unusual shape may indicate that it contains a fossil. What quarrymen call rotten flints, which are so hollow that they fall to pieces at the tap of a hammer, may be filled with a brownish powder; the microscope will show you that the grains are detached sponge-spicules and the skeletons of foraminifera.

Many of the chalk ammonites are strangely shaped. *Schloenbachia* has the usual spiral coils, but in *Scaphites* only the inner part of the shell is coiled, the rest

FIGURE 62. *The chalk ammonite* Turrilites

and some, *Marsupites* and *Uintacrinus*, had no holdfasts attaching them to the rocks but drifted loose in the sea.

Other Chalk Fossils

In the chalk the brachiopods *Terebratula* and *Rhynchonella* and the gasteropod *Pleurotomaria* are also found. The lamellibranch *Trigonia* is not so abundant as the molluscs *Inoceramus*, *Ostrea* and *Pecten*. There are few chalk corals, but you might find *Parasimilia*. Polyzoa encrust some of the fossils and, in the chalk, there are examples of the small tubes made by the

going off at a tangent and curling over like a hook. *Baculites* begins as a small flat spiral, the rest of the shell forming a long, narrow cone. *Turrilites* is a cone-shaped spiral. These are among the last of the ammonites, for they and the belemnites all died out in the Cretaceous, though the nautilus still lives in tropical seas.

As chalk began as a sediment on the sea-floor, you could hardly expect to find many land-plants in it. Rocks of similar age on the continent of Europe have yielded many fossil plants: not only conifers but such trees as oak, poplar, holly, maple, fig, walnut, beech, laurel, ivy and ilex. The Cretaceous woods must indeed have had quite a modern look.

Cretaceous Giant Reptiles

But though the Cretaceous woodlands may have seemed modern, this is more than can be said for the animals which roamed through them. One large tooth found in the Wealden beds of Sussex looked so much like that of the iguana, a modern American lizard, that the animal from which it came is called the *Iguanadon* (Iguana-toothed).

Many giant animals lived in America at this time. One of the strangest was *Triceratops*: about twenty-five feet long and ten feet high, it had a skull eight feet long, armed with the three horns which give the animal its name, and ending in a spiky frill. There were also many sea-serpents, including the forty-foot *Discosaurus*. Cretaceous forms the last bed in which the giant reptiles were found.

FIGURE 63. *The toothed seabird* Hesperornis

In this period, too, lived a new type of pterosaur, the *Pterodactyl* (Greek for finger-winged). This, of course, was a winged reptile, but there were also *Ichthyornis* (fish-bird) and the American *Hesperornis* (Western bird) which, although they had teeth, were in all other respects aquatic birds.

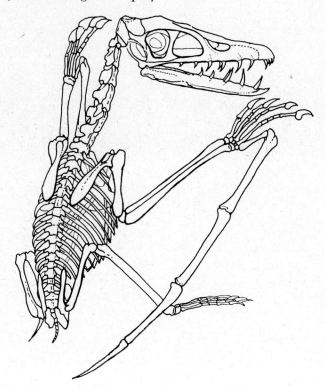

FIGURE 64. *A Pterodactyl skeleton*

CHAPTER XVII

The Age of Recent Life

THE TERTIARY and Quaternary Eras together amount to little more, either in thickness or in the time taken to form them, than any one of the other systems. Yet they are regarded as a distinct Era, the Cainozoic, because of the fossils, most of which are quite different from those in the Eras below. In the Tertiary we find plentiful remains of mammals; in the Quaternary, the remains and the handiwork of men.

The Dawn

Lyell divided the Tertiary into Systems, naming them from the proportion of modern types among their sea-shells. The oldest, in which this proportion is small, is the Eocene, the "Dawn of Recent" Life.

Most of the Tertiary rocks consist of soft or loose material, clays, sands and pebble-beds, with a few thin layers of limestone. In Eocene times, the sea in which the chalk was deposited retreated from England and, though it returned after some gentle earth movements, it now flowed more slowly and was shallower.

The Eocene sea was several times silted up by material brought into it by two large rivers, one flowing eastwards across southern England and the other north-westwords across France. Between these siltings-up, earth movements deepened the water and humped up the rocks in the Weald into an anticline.

In England, there are Eocene outcrops in two main areas. In south Hampshire and the northern part of the Isle of Wight,

sands and pebbles alternate with clays. Along the Thames are the Lower London Tertiaries, layers of pebbles and sand; above these is the London clay.

The fossils in these beds are very different from those in the chalk. The giant reptiles had died out; the Eocene

Fossil elephant-trunk from the Pleistocene—Barnsfield Pit, Swanscombe, Kent

reptiles were smaller, rather like crocodiles and snakes. Mammals, hitherto so scarce, were now abundant: the earlier ones, though very different from modern beasts, were small. Later, came others which, though not so huge and monstrous as the giant reptiles, were quite large and so clumsy and ugly you might think them mis-shapen.

Some of these early mammals distantly resembled the modern rhinoceros, tapir, lemur, pig and tiger. The earliest horse-like animal, *Eohippus* (dawn horse), was about the size of a fox, each of its legs ending not in one hoof but in several small toes.

As usual, the fossils you are most likely to find in the Eocene are those of the invertebrates and plants. Sharks' teeth are also present, and you may find traces of the last ganoid fish.

These fossils show how different the British climate was from that of today, for they include the remains of *tropical* animals and plants. Along with such familiar trees as the evergreens, oak, willow and maple, you may find traces of the palm, fig, cinnamon, aloe and eucalyptus, as well as fossil cacti. These include leaves, fruits and fragments of wood, some bored into by the so-called ship-worm—it is really a mollusc—*Teredo*.

Not only the great reptiles but many of the smaller creatures were completely

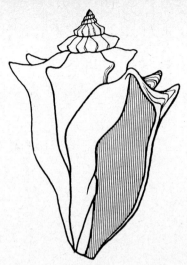

FIGURE 66.   *The Tertiary mollusc* Voluta

extinct or very scarce in Cainozoic times. There were no ammonites or belemnites, and nautilus lived only in tropical waters; the ganoid fish, too, were dying out.

Sea-lilies were less plentiful than sea-urchins, mostly of tropical or semi-tropical types: *Hemiaster* and *Schizaster* resemble the "fairy hearts" of the chalk.

Brachiopods, akin to the modern *Lingula* and *Terebratula*, were less plentiful than lamellibranchs, which differed from those in the chalk: *Trigonia* had almost vanished and the more common Eocene types are *Ostraea*, *Cyprina*, *Corbula* and *Nucula*. Many of the Eocene gasteropods, *Voluta*, *Thiara*, *Ceritheus* and *Turritella*, had ornamental shells; the opening of *Fusinus* and *Clavella* had a broad lip.

Tropical animals though they are, corals were rare in the Eocene, whose shallow seas were probably too muddy to suit them. You may, however, find the simple branching *Dendrophylla* or the compound *Litharea*.

Some of the Eocene forminifera are so large you can see them without a microscope. *Nummulites*, the "money fossil", is named from its shape; if you heat one of

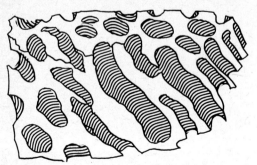

FIGURE 65.   *Wood bored into by "ship-worm", Teredo*

these "stone coins" over a spirit-lamp and drop it into cold water it may split across the middle; then the microscope will show you that, though the animal that built it consisted only of one cell, this is a spiral divided into many tiny compartments.

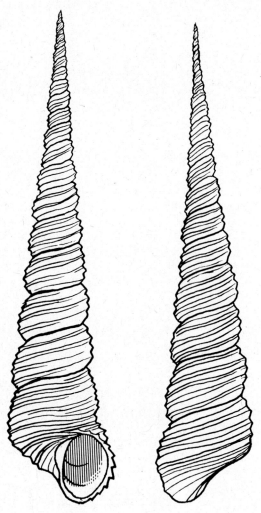

FIGURE 67. *The Tertiary mollusc* Turritella

Another unusually-shaped shell you may find in the Eocene is that of the mollusc *Scaphopod*. It is a narrow tube, almost straight or slightly curved, and open at both ends.

The Oligocene

The next Tertiary System, the Oligocene contains few recent fossils. During this period earth-movements sent the seas advancing and retreating across southern England, so that some of its rocks are of freshwater, others of brackish, and yet others of marine origin. Their largest outcrop in Britain is above the Eocene beds in south Hampshire and the northern part of the Isle of Wight.

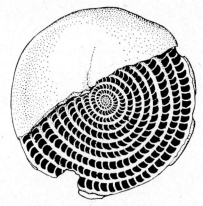

FIGURE 68. *The money fossil* Nummulites (*part of the surface has been removed to show the internal structure*)

The Oligocene mammals include the tapir-like *Palaeotherium* (ancient beast), the pig-like *Anthracotherium* and the *Hyaenadon*. As usual, invertebrate fossils are much more common.

Brachiopods had become very scarce and lamellibranchs plentiful: *Cyrena*, *Ostrea*, *Corbula* and *Mytilus*. Some of the gasteropods, like *Bulimus*, have tall, tapering spiral shells; some, like *Planorbis*, a flattened spiral; and some, like *Viviparus*, a shell resembling a snail's.

There are several interesting Oligocene beds in the Isle of Wight. On the northeast coast is a layer of shaly clay in which you may find fossil fish resembling small herrings, *Diplomytus*. Near Yarmouth there is an "insect bed" of limestone containing locusts, beetles, flies and ants, and

140

also spiders and leaves. In a "black band" of dark loam nearby are the seeds of aquatic plants, whose rootlets extend into the marls below; above this, a ledge in the cliffs is formed by the "water-lily bed", a clay in which are the roots and leaves of water-lilies and palms.

Near Bovey Tracy in Devon are other Oligocene beds: sands, freshwater clays and lignite (brown coal) containing plants similar to those which grow in the ravines nearby and on Dartmoor. The lava-flows of the Island of Mull off the west coast of Scotland are interbedded with sands and shales containing plants of Oligocene age, or thereabouts; in these "leaf beds" you may discover fossils of the gingko and sequoia trees.

The Miocene

Many geologists believe that the next System, which Lyell called the Miocene because its fossils are less recent, has no outcrop anywhere in Britain. Others think that the Bovey Tracy beds and one or two others may belong to this period.

During this period, the British Isles were raised above sea-level by tremendous earth movements. So powerful were these that they produced many of the Old World's greatest mountain ranges, from the Himalayas to the Alps; and, in Britain, which was on the fringe of the disturbance, they gave the Mesozoic beds their gentle south-easterly dip and bent those in south-east England into a succession of ridges and dips. They formed the Thames Valley syncline and the Wealden anticline, another syncline below Salisbury and Chichester, another anticline near Portsmouth, and the monocline which became the central ridge of the Isle of Wight and the Purbeck cliffs.

During this period, fissure eruptions in the Western Isles of Scotland and north-west Ireland emitted torrents of molten rock. Splitting into prismatic columns as it cooled, this became the basalt of Staffa and the Giant's Causeway.

Miocene fossils discovered in other lands include those of the elephant-like *Mastodon* and *Tetrabelodon*; the sabre-tooth tiger: the rhinoceros, deer, and ape; the *Oxydactylus*, something like a camel and something like a giraffe; and the horse-like *Neohipparion*.

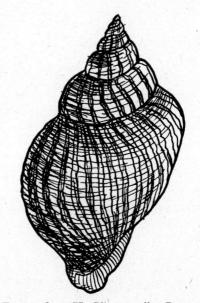

FIGURE 69. *The Pliocene mollusc* Purpura

The Pliocene

The Pliocene, whose fossils are more recent, was formerly thought to have produced most of the shelly sands, called Crag, of the East Anglian coast, and there are a few small outcrops of this System on the North Downs and in Cornwall. When these were formed, England was slowly sinking into the sea and its climate getting colder.

The conglomerate at the base of the crag contains brown sandstone pebbles, "boxstones", which when split open disclose fossil casts. It also contains flints, fossil shells and nodules from the London clay.

Next comes the Coralline Crag, coralines being a former name for the sea-mats, the polyzoa which it contains. Its other fossils include rather large brachiopod *Terebratula*, such molluscs as *Pecten*, sea-urchins, barnacles, corals and fish.

In the iron-tinted sands of the red crag above, you may find teeth not only of sharks but of *Mastodons* and whales. One of its gasteropods, *Neptunea*, is exceptional because its shell has a left-handed, instead of the usual right-handed, twist.

FIGURE 70. *The Pliocene mollusc* Buccinum

Further north, and larger than the other beds, is the Norwich crag. A layer of puddingstone at its base contains the bones of horse-like and elephant-like animals, and of sabre-tooth tigers, bears, wolves and beavers. The molluscs of this bed and of the Cromer beds above it are so like the modern ones that the only way of telling which is which is to notice which came from the crag and which seem to have been washed up recently by the tide.

Between two layers of freshwater clays in the Cromer series is the Forest Bed, consisting of the clays, sands and gravels of a former estuary. Besides the remains of mammals, many of which are extinct, it contains drifted tree-roots and branches and masses of peat.

The Pleistocene Cold Spell

Some geologists now think that much of the crag is not Pliocene at all but belongs to the next System, the Pleistocene. This is the lower of the two Quaternary Systems and its fossils, though they include some extinct species, are mostly recent.

This period opened in a time of growing cold. The mountain snows deepened and widened, and a sheet of ice spread widely over the land. The Great Ice Age had begun. Perhaps it was the weight of the accumulated ice which depressed Britain until the Scottish coast was below sea-level.

After some fluctuations in temperature, the climate became milder and the ice-covering melted. Either because of the removal of its weight or for some other reason, the land rose—or possibly the sea-level fell—until Britain stood higher above the water than it does now. Much of its surface had become almost a desert, like the Siberian tundra; later it became a grass-land resembling the Russian steppes; then dense forests spread across it until they were artificially cleared in modern times.

The traces which the Great Ice Age left on the scenery are many. Its invertebrate fossils, those of the Pleistocene, were so very like modern types that you would find them hard to distinguish.

Other fossils show, however, that the Pleistocene mammals were very different from those of today, as you would expect from the bleak conditions which they had to endure. On the fringes of the ice-fields, and in sheltered holes and corners, lived such creatures as the woolly mammoth and rhinoceros, the reindeer and the cave bear.

You have read about fossil rain-prints and ripple-marks. On the Norfolk coast, east of Sheringham is what you might call a fossil glacier. Though the ice which produced it has long since melted away, the imprint of its structure is clearly shown in the twisted layers of clay which form the cliff.

Bone-caves and Cave-men

Short though it is, only about a million years, the Quaternary deserves to be regarded as a separate System because in

FIGURE 71. *The skeleton of an extinct Irish elk. Its antlers had a span of more than three yards*

The Holocene—Our Time

The Great Ice Age ushered in the Holocene (wholly recent) period, also simply called the Recent, the one in which we live. The land is still being destroyed by weather, river and sea; sediment is still accumulating to form new lands; volcanoes are still erupting; earthquakes and gentle earth movements are still taking place. As Lyell explained, the causes which formed the earth's surface are still in operation.

it there developed a new geological force. Its insignificant beginnings were first realised through a study of some of the caves.

The first British cave to be scientifically studied, in 1816 by Joseph Whitbey, was Oreston, near Plymouth; in 1823 the results of this new branch of geology were summed up by the Rev. William Buckland. He explained that some of the caves were former hyaena dens, into which the animals had dragged the carcasses of their prey, whose horns and bones had been buried by the slowly-accumulating drip-stone. Though these fossils were not, as Buckland supposed, relics of the Flood (that, in Latin, was the title of his book) they show what sort of animals, some of them now extinct, lived in Britain long ago.

In 1840, a French cave was found to have the outline of an animal sketched on its walls. Since then, many other decorated caves have been found. A number of caves used to be inhabited by prehistoric men, who not only left the remains of some of the animals they hunted among the debris on the floor of the cave, but painted or sketched them upon the walls of the deeper caverns which they seem to have used for magical purposes. As these animals include mammoths, woolly rhinoceroses and reindeer, they show that towards the end of the Great Ice Age groups of human beings were coming into Europe.

Man Moulds the Landscape

Helped by the minerals in the rocks—first flint, then the ores of copper, tin and iron and now of uranium—human beings became civilised and the more they advanced the more powerful they became as a geological agent, a force able to change not only the landscape but the rocks below it. They destroy forests and plant new ones, turn the soil into a dust-bowl or bind and irrigate it to convert the wilderness into fertile land. They change the courses of rivers and dam their valleys to form new lakes. They excavate great gaps in the hills, and reinforce the coast with concrete to protect it from destruction by the sea. By releasing the energy of the atom, and applying it to peaceful purposes instead of to destruction, they may transform the earth's surface in ways which we cannot as yet foresee.